University of Texas at Arlington

COLLEGE

ALGEBRA

Patricia P. Ellington
Department of Mathematics
University of Texas at Arlington

Custom Publishing

New York   Boston   San Francisco
London   Toronto   Sydney   Tokyo   Singapore   Madrid
Mexico City   Munich   Paris   Cape Town   Hong Kong   Montreal

Cover Art: Courtesy of PhotoDisc/Getty Images.

Printed in the United States of America

10 9 8 7 6 5 4

2009361246

JP

**Pearson
Custom Publishing**
is a division of

www.pearsonhighered.com

ISBN 10: 0-558-39575-9
ISBN 13: 978-0-558-39575-9

College Algebra

CHAPTER 1

Functions, Graphs and Math Models

Section 1.1 Functions

Functions:

A function can be described as a relationship between an input number and an output number. Functions are commonplace in everyday life and show up in a variety of forms. A function can be represented as a set of ordered pairs, a graph, an equation or a table (which can be reduced to ordered pairs).

If we define a relationship using ordered pairs we are showing a correspondence between the first and second coordinates of the ordered pairs. We can graph the ordered pairs and also see the relationship. An equation can also represent the correspondence.

An example of a function in equation form is

$$y = 5x$$

In this example, y is a function of x.

We call x the **independent variable** and y the **dependent variable**.

Each time we replace x with a number we will find a unique value for y.

The various input values that we assign to x is called the **domain** and the possible resulting values of y is called the **range** of our function.

For each member of the domain (sometimes called elements) there is only one member of the range that corresponds to the given domain member.

Another way of describing a function is to say that for each member of the domain (our input choices) there is a unique resulting member from the range (our output results).

Function: A function is a correspondence between one set, the domain, and a second set, the range, that assigns to each element of the domain only one element of the range.

Example 1: Which of the given correspondences is a function:

    a. $2 \rightarrow 4$ $-8 \rightarrow 64$ $0 \rightarrow 0$
        $-2 \rightarrow 4$ $8 \rightarrow 64$

    b. Christmas $\rightarrow$ December 25
        April Fools $\rightarrow$ April 1
        New Years Day $\rightarrow$ January 1
        Independence Day $\rightarrow$ July 4
        Thanksgiving $\rightarrow$ November 24
        Thanksgiving $\rightarrow$ November 28

c.	Domain:	Correspondence	Range
	real numbers	squared numbers	a subset of the real numbers

d.	Domain:	Correspondence	Range
	all city names in US	in what state	all states in US

Solution:

    a. This correspondence is a function because each member of the domain corresponds to only one member of the range. It is okay for two different members of the domain to correspond to the same range member.

    b. This correspondence is not a function because one member of the domain correspond to different members in the range.

    c. This correspondence is a function because each real number has only one squared value.

    d. This correspondence is not a function because a city name can exist in more than one state.

If a correspondence between two sets is not a function, it can be an example of a **relation**.

Relation: A **relation** is a correspondence between a first set, the **domain**, and a second set, the **range**, so that each member of the domain corresponds to **at least one** member of the range. (Domain members can correspond to several range members).

Notice: In Example 1 all of the correspondences are relations, but not all of them are functions.

Example 2: Which of the given relations is a function? Define the domain and range.
  a. (6, 3), (6, 4), (5, 8)
  b. (1, 2), (2, 3), (3, 4)
  c. (4, 2), (16, – 4), (5, 2)

Solution:
  a. Not a function because two different ordered pairs have the same first coordinate and different second coordinates.
Domain: set of first coordinates: 6 and 5
Range: set of second coordinates: 3, 4 and 8

  b. Is a function since no ordered pairs have the same first coordinate.
Domain: set of first coordinates: 1, 2 and 3
Range: set of second coordinates: 2, 3 and 4

  c. Is a function since no ordered pairs have the same first coordinate. Note that two different first coordinates may correspond to the same second coordinate.
Domain: set of first coordinates: 4, 16 and 5
Range: set of second coordinates: 2 and – 4

Functional Notation: We often see functions represented by equations. We perform calculations to determine the range value that corresponds with a given domain value.

Given Equation: $y = x^2 - 5x + 4$. We can input values for x (domain values) into the given equation and get values for y (range values).

For $x = 1$ $y = (1)^2 - 5(1) + 4$ or $y = 0$

For $x = 2$ $y = (2)^2 - 5(2) + 4$ or $y = -2$

For $x = -1$ $y = (-1)^2 - 5(-1) + 4$ or $y = 10$

Using functional notation we will call the function f and we will use x to represent our input values and our output values we call $f(x)$. Most often functions have names of f, g or h. The term $f(x)$ is stated as "f of x" or "the value of f at x" or "f at x".

Changing to functional notation, the equation above would be described as:

$$f(x) = x^2 - 5x + 4$$

8

Our results would be:

$$f(1) = (1)^2 - 5(1) + 4 \qquad \text{thus } f(1) = 0$$

$$f(2) = (2)^2 - 5(2) + 4 \qquad \text{thus } f(2) = -2$$

$$f(-1) = (-1)^2 - 5(-1) + 4 \qquad \text{thus } f(-1) = 10$$

Example 3: If $f(x) = 2x^2 - 2x + 4$, find each of the following:

    a. $f(-2)$ b. $f(0)$

    c. $f(3b)$ d. $f(s+2)$

Solution: Think of $f(x) = 2x^2 - 2x + 4$ as: $f(?) = 2(?)^2 - 2(?) + 4$

To solve these we replace the ? with any number we want.

    a. $f(-2) = 2(-2)^2 - 2(-2) + 4$ or $f(-2) = 16$

    b. $f(0) = 2(0)^2 - 2(0) + 4$ or $f(0) = 4$

    c. $f(3b) = 2(3b)^2 - 2(3b) + 4 = 2(9b^2) - 6b + 4 = 18b^2 - 6b + 4$

    d. $f(s+2) = 2(s+2)^2 - 2(s+2) + 4$
$$= 2(s^2 + 4s + 4) - 2s - 4 + 4$$
$$= 2s^2 + 8s + 8 - 2s$$
$$= 2s^2 + 6s + 8$$

Example 3 can be solved using a graphing calculator. See Chapter 6, Example 1

Graphs of Functions:

We can graph a function just like we graph equations. We find ordered pairs as $(x, f(x))$ and plot these points and then sketch the graph.

Example 4: Graph the following.
    a. $f(x) = x^2 - 4$
    b. $f(x) = x^3 - 3x$

Solution:

    a. $f(x) = x^2 - 4$

Using points $(x, f(x))$, we will plot points and sketch the graph.

x	$f(x)$	$(x, f(x))$
-3	5	$(-3, 5)$
-2	0	$(-2, 0)$
-1	-3	$(-1, -3)$
0	-4	$(0, -4)$
1	-3	$(1, -3)$
2	0	$(2, 0)$
3	5	$(3, 5)$

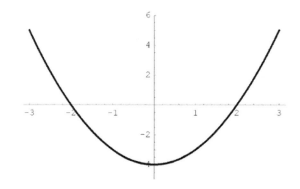

    b. $f(x) = x^3 - 3x$: Again plot points:

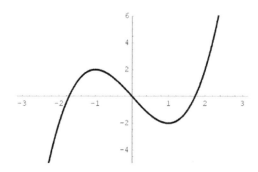

We can use a graphing calculator to check our graphs.

We can also find the value of a function by reading the graph.

Locate an input value on the *x*-axis and then move up or down vertically to the graph, and then read the value of the graph at that point on the *y*-axis. Look at the graph of $f(x) = x^3 - 3x$ above.

To find $f(-2)$ we can locate $x = -2$, move down to the function graph and then read the *y* value on the *y*-axis. We find that $f(-2) = -2$.

When we discussed the definition of a function we noted that each member in the domain can point to only one value in the range. Thus, each *x*-value can have only one *y*-value. If any *x*-value points to two *y*-values, we do not have a function. Note that two points with the same *x* coordinate would be vertically above/below each other. Keep this in mind as we study the vertical line test.

The Vertical-Line Test: This test can be used to determine if a relation is a function. The graph of a set of points is the graph of a function if every vertical line intersects the graph in at most one point.

The best way to use the vertical-line test is to try to find any vertical line that will cross the graph more than once. If none exists, then the graph represents a function. The definition states that every vertical line intersects the graph of a function in at most one point.

Example 5: Which of the graphs below is the graph of a function?

a.

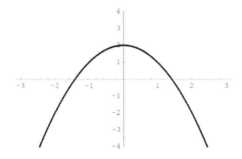

b.

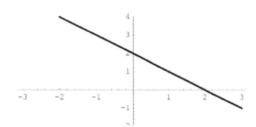

c.

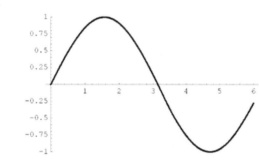

d.

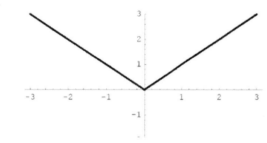

Solutions:

All graphs are graphs of functions because there is no vertical line that can be drawn that crosses the graph more than once.

Domain of a Function:

The domain of a function is the set of all numbers that can be input into the function which will result in output results of real numbers. If a number is substituted into the function and the result in not defined then that number is not a part of the domain.

In many cases, we can simply remember that the **domain is the set of x-values** and the **range is the set of y-values**. These can be specific numbers, intervals, or the set of all real numbers.

Example 6: For each of the given functions find the function value and then determine if the value is in the domain:

    a. $f(x) = \dfrac{1}{x-4}$ find $f(2)$ and $f(4)$

    b. $f(x) = \sqrt{x} - 14$ find $f(9)$ and $f(-4)$

Solution:

    a. $f(2) = \dfrac{1}{-2} = -\dfrac{1}{2}$ this is a real number and so 2 is in the domain of f.

    $f(4) = \dfrac{1}{0}$ this is not a real number since you cannot divide by zero

                  so 4 is not in the domain of f.

    b. $f(9) = \sqrt{x} - 14 = 3 - 14 = -11$ this result is a real number, and so 9 is in the domain of f.

    $f(-4) = \sqrt{-4} - 14$ the result is not defined because we cannot take the square root of a negative number, and -4 is not in the domain of f.

Example 7. Find the domain of the following functions:

    a. $f(x) = \dfrac{1}{x-2}$ notice that this is a fraction, so look for values that would make the denominator become zero

    b. $f(x) = \dfrac{x^2-9}{x^2-4}$ this is a fraction, so what values give a denominator of zero?

    c. $f(x) = x^2 - 4$

Solution:

    a. Since 2 will result in a denominator of zero, 2 cannot be in the domain. The domain is all real numbers except 2 and can be written as $(-\infty, 2) \cup (2, \infty)$

    b. Since this is a fraction, we must look for values that make the denominator zero. Factoring the denominator gives $(x+2)(x-2)$. x^2-4 would be zero if x is 2 or -2. These two numbers are not in

13

the domain of f.
The domain is $(-\infty, -2) \cup (-2, 2) \cup (2, \infty)$

c. This contains no fraction and no square root, so we can use any real number and the function will be defined. Thus the domain is all real numbers.

Finding the Domain and Range using a Graph:

We know that the domain is the set of all values that can be input into the function. These are x-values, and x-values are found along the x-axis of the graph.

The range is the set of all values that can be the output of the function. These are y-values and are found along the y-axis of the graph.

When we look at the graph of a function we can often determine the domain and range.

Example 8: Graph the given functions and see if you can determine the domain and range.

a. $f(x) = \dfrac{1}{x-3}$ b. $f(x) = x^3$ c. $f(x) = x^2 + 1$

Solutions

a.

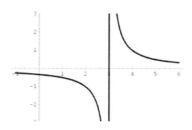

Domain $= (-\infty, 3) \cup (3, \infty)$
Range $= (-\infty, 0) \cup (0, \infty)$

14

b.

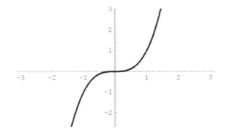

Domain = all real numbers
Range = all real numbers

c:

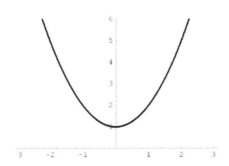

Domain = all real numbers
Range = $[1, \infty)$

Section 1.1 Exercises

In Exercises 1 — 12, is the correspondence a function?

1. $a \rightarrow p$ 2. $p \rightarrow z$ 3. $-4 \rightarrow 16$
   $b \rightarrow s$ $r \rightarrow y$ $-3 \rightarrow 9$
   $c \rightarrow t$ $s \rightarrow x$ $4 \rightarrow 16$

4. $3 \rightarrow 5$ 5. $t \rightarrow A$ 6. $p \rightarrow m$
   $2 \rightarrow 6$ $r \rightarrow C$ $q \rightarrow m$
   $1 \rightarrow 7$ $p \rightarrow E$ $r \rightarrow m$
   $1 \rightarrow 8$ $m \rightarrow C$ $s \rightarrow n$

Domain	Correspondence	Range
7. Set of seats in an arena	Each seat's row and number	A set of numbers and letters
8. Set of houses in one block	Each house's address number	A set of numbers
9. A set of family members	Each person's age	A set of numbers
10. A set of members of a basketball team	Each person's height	A set of numbers
11. A set of cars in a garage	Each car's color	A set of colors
12. A set of class members	GPA of each student	A set of numbers

A graph of a function is shown. Find the indicated function values.

13. $f(1), f(3),$ and $f(4)$

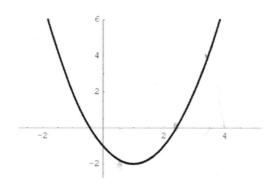

14. $g(-2)$, $g(0)$, and $g(4)$

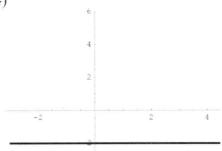

15 $t(-2)$, $t(0)$, and $t(1)$

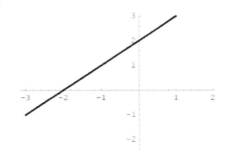

16. Given: $g(x) = 2x^2 + 3x - 4$, find each of the following.
   a) $g(0)$ b) $g(3)$ c) $g(-2)$ d) $g(-t)$

17. Given: $f(x) = x^2 + 3x$, find each of the following.
   a) $f(0)$ b) $f(-1)$ c) $f(5)$ d) $f(3m)$

18. Given: $h(x) = 2x^3$, find each of the following.
   a) $h(-2)$ b) $h(1)$ c) $h(p)$ d) $h(-y)$

19. Given: $s(x) = \dfrac{x+2}{x-1}$ find each of the following

   a) $s(-2)$ b) $s(0)$ c) $s(1)$ d) $s(\frac{1}{3})$

20. Given: $f(x) = \dfrac{x-3}{x}$ find each of the following.

   a) $f(3)$ b) $f(y+2)$ c) $f(0)$ d) $f(m^2)$

21. Given: $h(x) = |x| + 2$ find each of the following.
   a) $h(-2)$ b) $h(-3)$ c) $h(p)$ d) $h(0)$

22. Given: $f(x) = x^3 - x^2$ find each of the following.
   a) $f(-1)$ b) $f(-2)$ c) $f(3y)$ d) $f(1/2)$
23. Given: $d(x) = 2x^2 + 3x - 4$ find each of the following.

17

a) $d(2)$ b) $d(-1)$ c) $d(2m)$ d) $d(0)$

Find the domain of the given functions for problems $24 - 37$.

24. $f(x) = 5x + 2$

25. $f(x) = 2\left|4x - 3\right|$

26. $f(x) = 3 + \dfrac{4}{x}$

27. $f(x) = 0$

28. $f(x) = \dfrac{5.0}{3 - x}$

29. $f(x) = \dfrac{x + 8}{x^2}$

30. $f(x) = \dfrac{x^2 - 4}{x^2 - 9}$

31. $f(x) = x^3 + x^2$

32. $f(x) = \sqrt{4 - x}$

33. $f(x) = 1/3\left|x\right|$

34. $f(x) = x^2 + 3$

35. $f(z) = \dfrac{\sqrt{x + 2}}{2x}$

36. $f(x) = \dfrac{x^2 - 3x + 2}{x^2 + x - 6}$

37. $f(x) = \sqrt{x^2 + 1}$

Sections 1.2 Linear Functions, Lines and Slope

Linear Functions:

A line function is a function whose equation is a straight line.

A linear function is a function that can be transformed into:

$$f(x) = mx + b$$

where x is any real number and m and b are constants.

A **constant function** is a function in the form $f(x) = mx + b$ where m equals zero. Thus a **constant function takes the form $f(x) = b$.**

The identity function is a function in the form $f(x) = mx + b$ where $m = 1$ and $b = 0$. The **identity function is written as: $f(x) = x$**

The graph of the identity function: $y = x$

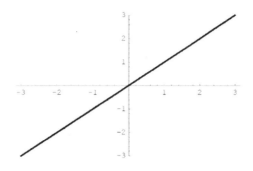

The graph of a constant function: $y = 3$

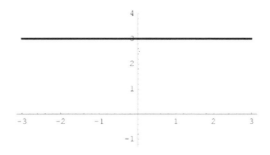

> **Horizontal Lines:**
>
> 1. Horizontal lines are parallel to the *x*-axis.
> 2. These lines are defined by an equation in the form: $y = b$.
>
> These lines are functions and may be written as $f(x) = b$.

> **Vertical Lines:**
>
> 1. Vertical lines are parallel to the *y*-axis.
> 2. These lines are defined by an equation in the form: $x = a$.
>
> These lines are NOT functions.

Slope and Linear Functions:

When we discuss the slope of a line we are talking about the steepness of the line. It can be defined as a fraction with the numerator as the vertical change, called the rise of a line, and the denominator as the corresponding horizontal change, the run of a line.

> **The slope m of a line containing the distinct points $P_1(x_1, y_1)$ and $P_2(x_2, y_2)$ is given by:**
>
> $$m = \frac{change\ in\ y}{change\ in\ x}$$
>
> $$= \frac{rise}{run}$$
>
> $$= \frac{y_2 - y_1}{x_2 - x_1}$$

Example 1: Graph the function $f(x) = -5/2x + 4$ and find its slope.

Solution: The function is a linear function because it is given in the linear form. We then know that the graph is a straight line and we only need two points to be able to draw the graph.

We can pick two different values for x and then get the corresponding y-value, and thus w have two points on the line.

$$f(0) = -5/2(0) + 4 = 4 \qquad \rightarrow \qquad \text{Point } (0,4)$$

$$f(2) = -5/2(2) + 4 = -1 \qquad \rightarrow \qquad \text{Point } (2, -1)$$

$$m = \frac{y_2 - y_1}{x_2 - x_1} = \frac{-1-4}{2-0} \rightarrow m = \frac{-5}{2} = -\frac{5}{2}$$

Graph the line using the two points and count the rise over run:

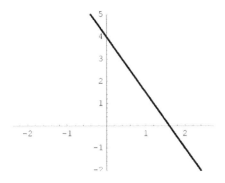

We could have chosen other points, and the slope would have been the same. Pick two more points and see if you find the same slope for the given function.

Notice that we calculated the slope to be $-5/2$ and that is the value of m in the equation:

$$m = -5/2 \qquad \text{and} \qquad f(x) = -5/2x + 4.$$

The function given by $f(x) = mx + b$ has a slope of m .

General rules about the slope of a line:

Vertical line → slope is undefined or has "no slope"

Horizontal line → slope is zero

A line that slants upward from left to right → positive slope

A line that slants down from left to right→ negative slope

The steeper a line is, the larger the absolute value of the slope will be

Remember that a slope of zero is not at all the same as "no slope". When we say "no slope" we mean that the slope cannot be calculated and is undefined.

Applications of Slope:

We find the use of slope in many real-world applications.

When driving in the mountains the steepness (or slope) of a road on the mountains are given in highway signs as the grade so that drivers will be aware of the rise or fall of the road and can reduce their gear if necessary. Signs that say 5% grade are stating that the road ahead will rise or fall 5 feet vertically for every 100 feet. Highway standards require that interstate or state highways have maximum limits for road grades.

A treadmill uses the same concept of steepness or slope. The walker on a treadmill will raise the slant of the treadmill in order to increase his heart rate and aerobic levels. Most treadmills have a grade (slope) 0 which is flat up to 8 or 10 which is rather steep.

Access ramps for wheelchair use must adhere to standards of grade or slope. The laws state that the maximum steepness of these ramps cannot exceed 1 foot rise for every 12 feet of horizontal run. The slope defined by "rise over run" would be 1/12.

Example 3: Sketch a line through point $P(0, -3)$ that has a slope of 4/3.

Solution: An easy way to work this problem is to start by graphing the point $(0, -3)$ then we can obtain a second point by using the slope.

Move to the right using the denominator of *m* since that is the horizontal change.

Next we will either move up or down using the numerator:

If *m* is positive, we will move up.

If *m* is negative we will move down.

In this example we will move right 3 and up 4.

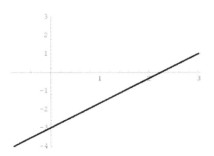

Example 4: Sketch a line

a) through the point P(1, 7/2) that has a slope of
$m = 0$

b) through the point P(2, 3) and the slope is undefined

Solution: Start with the given point and mark this point on the graph.
a) Since the slope is zero, we know that this will be a horizontal line. So, we draw a horizontal line at the given point.

a)

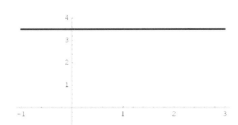

b) Since the slope is undefined, we know that the line will be a vertical line. Draw a vertical line at the given point.

b)

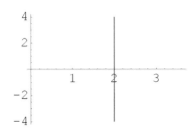

To Find Slope:

Given a graph → count rise over run

Given 2 points → use formula $m = \dfrac{y_2 - y_1}{x_2 - x_1}$

Given equation → put into $y = mx+b$ form and then m = slope

Section 1.2 Exercises

Find the slope of the lines shown on the given graphs.

1.

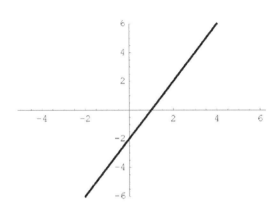

2.

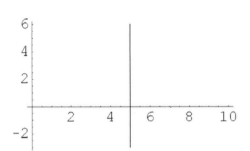

3.

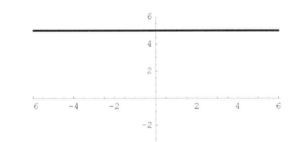

4.

5.

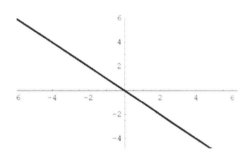

6.

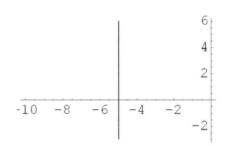

Find the slope of the line, given 2 points.

7. $(4,1)$ and $(-3, 2)$ 8. $(-2,5)$ and $(-4,-5)$ 9. $(-2,-1)$ and $(-5,-9)$

10. $(.4, .3)$ and $(.7, .4)$ 11. $(1/3,-1/8)$; $(2/3,-7/8)$ 12. $(5.12,3.14)$ and $(0,0)$

13. $(2,6)$ and $(3,6)$ 14. $(1,-4)$ and $(1,4)$ 15. $(-2,-3)$ and $(-1,1)$

16. $(0, 0)$ and $(1, 1)$ 17. $(-9,-4)$ and $(-9, 4)$ 18. $(0, 0)$ and $(-3,-4)$

19. $(4.5, 0)$ and $(3.7, 1.3)$

Graph the equation and find the slope.

20. $y = -3x + 2$ 21. $y = \frac{3}{2}x - 5$

22. $y = 4$ 23. $x = 4$

24. $x + 2y = 8$ 25. $2y - 4x = 6$

26. $y = 1.5x - 2$ 27. $y = -1/3x + 3$

28. $x = -4$

29. $y = -2/3$

30. $2x - y = 4$

31. $x + \dfrac{1}{2}y = 3$

Section 1.3 Linear Equations

Slope-Intercept Form of an Equation:

The graph of $y = mx + b$ is a line with:

slope = m
y-intercept of $(0, b)$

Notice: slope is a number and does not contain a variable.

.

If we rewrite the equation of a line so that it is in slope-intercept form, we see that the slope m is the coefficient of x.

Example 1: What is the slope and y-intercept of the line with the equation:

$$y = 2/3 \, x + 14$$

Solution: Since the equation is in the form $y = mx + b$, we need only look at the equation and find the slope and y-intercept.

The coefficient of x is 2/3 which is the slope.

The number 14 is the b term and gives us the y-intercept.

Since the y-intercept is the place where the graph crosses the y-axis, the value of x at this point is zero.

$$m = 2/3 \qquad\qquad y\text{-intercept} = (0,14)$$

A linear equation is any equation whose graph is a straight line.

To find the slope of a line, we solve the equation for y. The equation is now in slope-intercept form, which is:

$$y = mx + b$$

and the slope is m and the y-intercept is $(0,b)$.

Example 2: What is the slope and y-intercept of the line with the equation?

$$4x - 2y = 5$$

Solution: Since we are given an equation, the method used to find the slope is to rewrite the equation in slope-intercept form. We do this by solving the given equation for y:

$$4x - 2y = 5 \qquad \text{given equation}$$
$$-2y = -4x + 5 \qquad \text{subtract } 4x \text{ from both sides}$$
$$y = 2x - 5/2 \qquad \text{divide both sides of the equation by } -2$$

Reading the changed equation for m and b:

slope is 2   and   the y-intercept is $(0, -5/2)$.

We can write the equation of a line if we know the slope and y-intercept.

Example 3: Find the equation of a line given a slope of ¾ and y-intercept of $(0, 6)$

Solution: We will use the slope-intercept form to write the equation.

Use ¾ as m and 6 as b.

$$y = mx + b$$
$$y = \text{¾} \, x + 6$$

Example 4: Find the equation of a line with slope of $-1/3$ containing the point $(-6, 3)$

Solution: Notice that this problem did not give the y-intercept. Use the slope-intercept form to find the equation, and then we will use the slope and point to find the y-intercept:

$y = mx + b$ Slope-intercept form of equation

$y = (-1/3)x + b$ Next, use the given point for x and y to find b.

$3 = (-1/3)(-6) + b$ Now we solve for b.

$3 = 2 + b$

$b = 1$

The equation of the line is $y = -1/3 x + 1$

We can also graph linear equations if we know the slope and y-intercept.

Example 5: Graph the equation:

$$y = 2/3 \, x - 2$$

Solution: Since the equation is in slope-intercept form, we know that the slope is 2/3 and the y-intercept is $(0, -2)$.

First plot the y-intercept.

Next use the slope, and remember that slope is rise/run.

Our denominator tells how many units to move horizontally to the right from the y-intercept, and then count up or down the number of units in the numerator.

If the slope is positive, count up; and if the slope is negative, count down.

Beginning at the y-intercept $(0, -2)$, count right 3 and up 2 to a second point.

The new point is $(3, 0)$.

Now draw the line between $(0, -2)$ and $(3, 0)$

Point-Slope Equation of a Line:

The point-slope equation of a line is most often used to find the equation of a line (or write the equation of a line).

Point-Slope Equation: An equation for the line through the point (x_1, y_1) with slope m is:

$$y - y_1 = m(x - x_1)$$

This equation is very important because it can be used to WRITE AN EQUATION.

If we know the slope of a line and one point that the line passes through, we can write the equation of the line using the point-slope equation.

Example 6: What is the equation of a line:

passing through the points (1, 2) and (2, 6)

Solution: When asked for an equation, it is easy to find the equation using the point-slope equation.

First find the slope: $m = \dfrac{y_2 - y_1}{x_2 - x_1} = \dfrac{6-2}{2-1} = 4$

Now use the point-slope equation with $m = 4$ and one of the points. Use (x, y) as the other point:

$$y - y_1 = 4(x - x_1)$$
$$y - 2 = 4(x - 1)$$
$$y - 2 = 4x - 4$$
$$y = 4x - 2$$

Parallel Lines:

Parallel Lines:

Non-vertical lines are parallel if and only if they have the same slopes but different y-intercepts.

Vertical lines are parallel.

Lines such as $x = 2$ and $x = 5$ are both vertical lines and thus are parallel.

Two non-vertical lines that have the same slope but different y-intercepts are parallel also.

For example:

$y = 3x + 4$ and $y = 3x + 7$ are two lines that have the same slope of 3.

These lines have different y-intercepts.

These two lines are parallel lines.

Perpendicular Lines:

Perpendicular Lines:

Two lines are perpendicular if one is a horizontal line $y = a$ and the other is a vertical line $x = b$.

Two lines with slope m_1 and m_2 are perpendicular if and only if
$$m_1 m_2 = -1$$

From this theorem we should realize that perpendicular lines have **slopes that are opposite reciprocals**.

Example 7: Determine whether the following pairs of lines are parallel, perpendicular, or neither:

a) $y + 3 = 6x$; $2y - 12x = 4$ b) $y + 1 = 2x$; $2y + x = 3$

c) $y + 2x = 4$; $2x = 5 + 2y$

Solution: Determine if the lines are perpendicular, parallel, or neither by looking at the slopes of each set of lines

a) The slope-intercept forms of these equations are: $y = 6x - 3$ and $y = 6x + 2$ Both lines have slope of 6 with different y-intercepts. These two lines are parallel.

b) The slope-intercept forms of these equations are: $y = 2x - 1$ and $y = -1/2x + 3/2$. One line has slope of 2, and the other has slope of $-1/2$. The product of these two slopes is -1, and these lines are perpendicular.

c) The slope-intercept forms of these equations are: $y = -2x + 4$ and $y = x - 5/2$. The lines have slopes of -2 and 1. The lines do not have the same slope and the product of the two slopes is not equal to -1. These lines are neither parallel nor perpendicular.

Example 8: Write the equation of a line that is parallel to the graph of the line

$2y - 4x = 8$ and contains the point (3, 2).

Solution: In order to write the equation of a line, use the point-slope equation

$$y - y_1 = m(x - x_1).$$

To use this equation, we need the slope of our line and a point on our line.

We have the given point, but we do not have the slope.

Find the slope of the line that is given, and since our line is parallel to the given line, use the same slope.

First transform the equation of the given line into slope-intercept form to get the slope.

Solve for y:

$$2y - 4x = 8$$

$$y = 2x + 4.$$

The slope of this line is 2 and we will use the slope of 2 with the point (3, 2).

$$y - y_1 = m(x - x_1)$$

$$y - 2 = 2(x - 3)$$

$$y - 2 = 2x - 6$$

$$y = 2x - 4$$

Example 9: Write the equation of a line that is perpendicular to the graph of the line $3y - x = 9$ and contains the point (4, 1).

Solution: In order to write the equation of a line, use the point-slope equation

$$y - y_1 = m(x - x_1).$$

To use this equation, we will need the slope of our line and a point on our line.

We have the given point, but we do not have the slope.

Find the slope of the line that is given, and since our line is perpendicular to the given line, we take the opposite reciprocal of the slope we find and use the result for our new line.

First transform the equation into slope-intercept form to find the slope.

Solve the given equation $3y - x = 9$ for y:

$$y = \frac{1}{3}x + 3.$$

The slope of the given line is $\frac{1}{3}$.

Our slope will be the opposite reciprocal which is -3 and our point is $(4,1)$:

$$y - y_1 = m(x - x_1)$$

$$y - 1 = -3(x - 4)$$

$$y - 1 = -3x + 12$$

$$y = -3x + 13$$

Line/Slope Information:

To find slope:	$m = \dfrac{y_2 - y_1}{x_2 - x_1}$	Use if given 2 points
	$m = \dfrac{rise}{run}$	Use to count a graph
	$y = mx + b$	Use this form to find slope of a given line

To write the equation of a line:
$$y - y_1 = m(x - x_1)$$

Horizontal line:	$y = b$
Vertical line:	$x = a$
Parallel lines:	Same slope
Perpendicular lines:	Slopes are opposite reciprocals

Mathematical Models:

Mathematical models can be used to give a mathematical description of a real-world situation. Mathematical models are used to help predict what will happen in a real-world situation. Often these models are graphs and equations.

Steps used with mathematical models are:

1. Define a real-world problem
2. Collect data
3. Plot this collected data
4. Construct a model that best represents the data
5. Use the model to predict

If the predictions turn out to be incorrect, the model must be changed or discarded. Many models are continuously being revised. For example, a mathematical model that gives an accurate prediction of length of life is changing frequently as medical treatments and medicines improve life expectancy.

Linear functions can sometimes be used as mathematical models. We try to find a function that represents with the greatest accuracy data from experimentation and observation, reasoning, and common sense. When we plot data, we see what is called a **scatterplot.** Then we try to find the equation of a line that best fits the data.

Linear Regression

> **Linear Regression**
> a process that finds a line of *best fit* of given data. The linear regression line is a unique line that best describes the behavior of data.

Calculators are used to find a linear regression for a given set of data. See Chapter 6, Example 2 for an example of finding a linear regression.

Section 1.3 Exercises

Find the slope and the *y*-intercept of the given equations:

1. $y = \dfrac{2}{5}x - 5$

2. $f(x) = -x + 4$

3. $y = 3/4$

4. $x = -\dfrac{2}{3}$

5. $f(x) = 7 - \dfrac{1}{2}x$

6. $y = 4 - \dfrac{2}{9}x$

7. $2x + 3y = 12$

8. $3x - 2y = 18$

9. $y = 3$

10. $x = 8$

11. $4x + 5y = 12$

12. $3x - 5y + 10 = 0$

Graph the given line using the slope and intercept method and the given equation:

13. $y = \dfrac{1}{4}x - 1$

14. $y = \dfrac{2}{3}x + 1$

15. $f(x) = 4x - 1$

16. $f(x) = -3x + 5$

17. $2x - 4y = 8$

18. $3x + 2y = -3$

19. $x + 3y = 15$

20. $4y - 6x = -4$

Write the equation of a line in slope-intercept form using the given.

21. $m = 4$, *y*-intercept $(0, 3)$

22. $m = -\dfrac{2}{3}$, *y*-intercept $(0, 2)$

23. $m = -3$, *y*-intercept $(0, 4)$

24. $m = \dfrac{2}{9}$, *y*-intercept $(0, 5)$

25. $m = -3.5$, *y*-intercept $(0, -2)$

26. $m = \dfrac{2}{5}$, contains $(3, -2)$

27. $m = -\dfrac{2}{3}$, contains $(4, 3)$

28. $m = 2$, contains $(1, -3)$

29. $m = -3$, contains $(-2, 3)$

30. $m = -\dfrac{3}{4}$, contains $(-1, -2)$

31. contains $(-1, 3)$ and $(2, 5)$

32. contains $(2, 0)$ and $(5, 7)$

33. contains $(6, 1)$ and $(-1, 4)$

34. Contains $(-2, 2)$ and $(-1, 3)$

35. Contains $(0, 5)$ and $(2, 3)$

36. Contains $(-3, 0)$ and $(0, 1)$

Write equations of the horizontal and vertical lines that pass through the given point:

37. $(0, -2)$

38. $\dfrac{-4}{5}, 1$

39. $(1, 2)$

40. $(0, 0)$

Are the pairs of lines parallel, perpendicular or neither?

41. $y = \dfrac{2}{3}x - 5$

$y = -\dfrac{2}{3}x + 5$

42. $y = \dfrac{3}{4}x - 5$

$y = 7 + .75x$

43. $y = -\dfrac{1}{4}x$

$y = -4x + 2$

44. $2x - 4y = -2$

$2x + 4y = 3$

45. $y = 4x - 6$

$4y = 8 - x$

46. $y = 4 - x$

$y = x + 6$

Write two equations in slope-intercept form for a line passing through the given point. One line is parallel to the given line, and the other is perpendicular to the given line.

47. $(-1, 4)$ $f(x) = 2x + 5$

48. $(3, 5)$ $y = \dfrac{2}{3}x + 2$

49. $(-3, -1)$ $2x + y = 6$

50. $(4, 2)$ $y = 2.4(x - 2) + 1$

51. $(3, -2)$ $x = -1$

52. $(3, -2)$ $y = -1$

True or false?

53. The lines $x = -2$ and $y = 4$ are perpendicular.

54. The lines $y = 3x + 4$ and $y = -3x + 5$ are parallel.

55. The lines $x = -1$ and $x = 1$ are perpendicular.

56. The lines $y = 2x + 4$ and $y = 2x - 4$ are perpendicular.

Section 1.4   Additional Functions

Increasing, Decreasing and Constant Functions

Terminology	Definitions	Graph
f is **increasing** on an interval	$f(x_1) < f(x_2)$ whenever $x_1 < x_2$	
f is **decreasing** on an interval	$f(x_1) > f(x_2)$ whenever $x_1 < x_2$	
f is **constant** on an interval	$f(x_1) = f(x_2)$ for every x_1 and x_2	

An example of an increasing function is any line with a positive slope and an example of a decreasing function is any line with a negative slope. An example of a constant function is $f(x) = c$ which is a horizontal line and has a slope of zero.

Example 1: Determine the intervals on which the function in the given figure is

    a . increasing   b. decreasing   c. constant

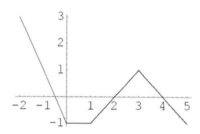

Solution:

    a. For x-values (domain values) from $x = 1$ to $x = 3$, the y-values (range values) increase from -1 to 1. The function is increasing on the interval $(1,3)$.

    b. For x-values from -2 to 0, y-values decrease; y-values also decrease for x-values 3 to 5. The function is decreasing on the intervals of $(-2, 0)$ and $(3, 5)$.

    c. For x-values from 0 to 1 the value of y is -1. The function is constant on the interval $(0, 1)$.

Curves:

Curves do not have slopes, but you will learn later that the slope of a line tangent to the graph of a curve at a point is used to determine if a function is increasing, decreasing, or constant at the point.

If the slope is found to be positive, the function is increasing at the point, and if the slope is found to be negative, the function is decreasing.

Slope cannot be both positive and negative at the same time, so the function cannot be both increasing and decreasing at the point.

This is the reason that **open** intervals are used to express increasing and decreasing functions.

Relative Maximum and Minimum Values.

Look at the graph:

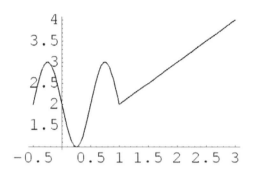

The graph has "highs" and "lows" at different *x*-values.

The values of the given function at $f(-0.25)$ and $f(0.75)$ are called **relative maxima (the plural of maximum is maxima).**

The value of the function at the point $f(0.25)$ is called a **relative minimum (the plural of minimum is minima).**

Relative Maxima and Minima

Given function *f(x)* and that *f(c)* exists for some *c*-value in the domain of *f*.

Then:
    f(c) has a relative maximum value in an open interval I containing c if
        f(c) > *f(x)*, for every *x* in I; and

    f(c) is a relative minimum value in an open interval I containing c if
        f(c)< *f(x)*. for every *x* in I.

An easy way to think of relative maximum and minimum is:
    If *f(c)* is the highest point in some open interval, then it is a relative maximum.
    If *f(c)* is the lowest point in some open interval, then it is a relative minimum.

In order to find relative maxima and minima in an algebra course a graphing calculator should be used. See Chapter 6, Example 3 for such a problem.

More Models of Functions:

Example 2: Two buses leave the same location at the same time. One travels East at a speed of 55 mph and the other travels North at a speed of 60 mph. Express the distance between the two buses as a function of time.

Solution 2: The easiest way to look at this problem is to draw a picture of the buses after a certain time like 2 hours.

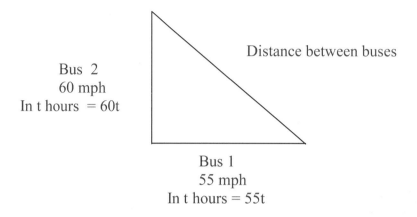

Bus 2
60 mph
In t hours = 60t

Distance between buses

Bus 1
55 mph
In t hours = 55t

We can find the distance that each bus travels by multiplying the mph by the number of hours.

Bus 1 would travel a distance of 55 mph times 2 hours which is 110miles.

Bus 2 would travel a distance of 60 mph times 2 hours which is 120 miles.

The figure is a right triangle, so the Pythagorean theorem will give the distance between them.

We will define the distance of Bus 1 as 55t where t is any amount of time and the distance of Bus 2 will be 60t.

The function can be represented as:

$$[d(t)]^2 = (55t)^2 + (60t)^2$$

$$d(t) = \sqrt{3025t^2 + 3600t^2} \quad = \quad \sqrt{6625t^2} \; = \; \cancel{89.3\pi} \; 81.39t$$

Since distance is never a negative number, we only use the positive root.

Example 3: A family has a small triangular plot to use for their garden. The base of the triangle to be used must be 3 times as long as the height of the triangle.

Define the Area of the plot as a function of the height.

Solution 3: First draw a picture of the garden plot.

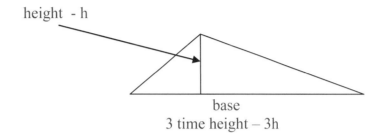

height - h

base
3 time height – 3h

Remember that the area of a triangle is found by: Area = ½ base times height

Call the height h, and since the base is 3 times the height, it becomes 3h.

The area function becomes:

$$A(h) = \frac{1}{2}(3h)(h)$$

$$= \frac{3}{2}h^2 \quad = 0.667h^2 \qquad \boxed{= 3/2h^2}$$

Section 1.4 Exercises:

Determine the intervals on which the function is increasing, decreasing and constant. Estimate any relative maxima or minima of the function.

1. $f(x) = x^2$

2. $f(x) = x^2 + 2$

3. $f(x) = x^2 - 3$

4. $f(x) = 4x$

5. $f(x) = 3$

6. $f(x) = |x|$

7. $f(x) = 2x + 1$

8. $f(x) = -2x + 1$

9. $f(x) = |x| + 2$

10. $f(x) = -|x|$

11. The Smiths have 100 feet of fencing with which to enclose a rectangular flower bed. If the bed is x feet long, express the bed's area as a function of the length.

12. The soccer team is designing a triangular flag for their games. The length of the base is 5 inches more that the height, h. Express the area of the flag as a function of the height.

13. An airplane is preparing to land at the local airport. The airplane's altitude is 5000ft. The slant distance from the plane to the airport is d feet. Express the horizontal distance h as a function of d.

14. A pool company is designing a rectangular pool. If the perimeter of the pool is 160 feet, and the length of the pool is x feet long, express the area of the pool as a function of the length.

15. A farmer has 400 yards of fencing to enclose a rectangular plot. If the width of the plot is w, express the area of the plot as a function of w.

Section 1.5 Function Algebra

In this section we will add, subtract, multiply and divide functions and obtain new functions.

Sums, Differences, Products and Quotients:

If $f(x) = x + 3$ and $g(x) = x^2$ then
$f(2) = 2 + 3 = 5$ and $g(2) = 4$

$f(2) + g(2) = 5 + 4 = 9$
$f(2) - g(2) = 5 - 4 = 1$
$f(2) * g(2) = 5 * 4 = 20$
and

$$\frac{f(2)}{g(2)} = \frac{5}{4}$$

Any sum, difference, product and quotient of $f(x)$ and $g(x)$ may be calculated as long as x is in the domain of **both** f and g and $g(x) \neq 0$ in the quotient $f(x)/g(x)$.

Sums, Differences, Products and Quotients of Functions

If f and g are functions and x is in the domain of both functions, then

$$(f + g)(x) = f(x) + g(x)$$

$$(f - g)(x) = f(x) - g(x)$$

$$(fg)(x) = f(x) * g(x)$$

$$\frac{f}{g}(x) = \frac{f(x)}{g(x)}, g(x) \neq 0$$

Example 1: Given that $f(x) = x + 2$ and $g(x) = \sqrt{x + 1}$.

Find   a. $(f + g)(x)$

         b. $(f + g)(4)$

         c. $(f + g)(-3)$

Solution:

     a. $(f + g)(x) = f(x) + g(x)$

               $= x + 2 + \sqrt{x + 1}$

     b. $f(4) = 4 + 2 = 6$ and $g(4) = \sqrt{4 + 1} = \sqrt{5}$

        $(f + g)(4) = f(4) + g(4)$

               $= 6 + \sqrt{5}$

     c. $f(-3) = -3 + 2 = -1$ and $g(-3) = \sqrt{-3 + 1} = \sqrt{-2}$ this is not a real number

        When we examine $g(x)$ we realize that -3 is not in the domain of $g(x)$.

        Thus, $(f + g)(-3)$ does not exist.

Domain of sum, difference, product:

The domain of $(f + g)(x)$, $(f - g)(x)$ and $(fg)(x)$ is the intersection of the domains of the functions f and g.

The intersection of two domains is the set of numbers that is in both domains.

Example 2: Given that $f(x) = x^2 - 9$ and $g(x) = x + 3$, find:

     a.   the domain of $(f + g)(x)$, $(f - g)(x)$, $(fg)(x)$ and $\dfrac{f}{g}(x)$

     b. $(f + g)(x)$ c. $(f - g)(x)$

     d. $(fg)(x)$ e. $(f/g)(x)$ f. $(gg)(x)$

Solution:

a. The domain of f is the set of all real numbers.

The domain of g is also the set of all real numbers.

The domain of $f+g$, $f-g$ and fg is the intersection of the domains of f and g. It is the set of numbers that are in **both** domains and for this example is the set of all real numbers.

The domain of f/g is also the intersection but it also must not include any numbers that would make the function g equal zero.

If $g(x) = x+3$, then $g(-3)$ would result in a denominator of zero.

Thus the domain must exclude -3 and is $(-\infty, -3) \cup (-3, \infty)$

b. $(f+g)(x) = f(x) + g(x) = (x^2 - 9) + (x+3) = x^2 + x - 6$

c. $(f-g)(x) = f(x) - g(x) = (x^2 - 9) - (x+3) = x^2 - x - 12$

d. $(f*g)(x) = f(x) * g(x) = (x^2 - 9)(x+3) = x^3 + 3x^2 - 9x - 27$

e. $(f/g)(x) = \dfrac{f(x)}{g(x)} = \dfrac{x^2 - 9}{x+3} = \dfrac{(x+3)(x-3)}{x+3} = x - 3, x \neq -3$

f. $(gg)(x) = g(x) * g(x) = (x+3)^2 = x^2 + 6x + 9$

Difference Quotient:

The Difference Quotient is defined as:
$\dfrac{f(x+h) - f(x)}{h}$ or $\dfrac{f(a+h) - f(a)}{h}$

The Difference Quotient or the average rate of change is used often in the study of calculus, and it is important to be able to find and simplify this quotient.

Example 3: For the function $f(x) = x^2 - 2x - 8$, find the difference quotient:
$$\frac{f(x+h) - f(x)}{h}.$$

Solution:
First we will find $f(x+h)$: We will replace x with $x+h$ in the given function.
$$\begin{aligned} f(x+h) &= (x+h)^2 - 2(x+h) - 8 \\ &= (x^2 + 2xh + h^2) - 2x - 2h - 8 \\ &= x^2 + 2xh + h^2 - 2x - 2h - 8 \end{aligned}$$

47

Now we will evaluate the Difference Quotient:

$$\frac{f(x+h)-f(x)}{h} =$$

$$= \frac{(x^2+2xh+h^2-2x-2h-8)-(x^2-2x-8)}{h}$$

$$= \frac{2xh-2h+h^2}{h}$$

$$= \frac{h(2x-2+h)}{h}$$

$$= 2x-2+h$$

Composite Functions:

> **The Composite Function** $f \circ g(x)$ of two functions f and g is defined by
>
> $$f \circ g(x) = f(g(x)).$$
>
> The domain of $f \circ g$ is the set of all x in the domain of g such that $g(x)$ is in the domain of f.

Example 4: Given $f(x) = 3x - 4$ and $g(x) = x^2 - 2x + 6$. Find:

     a. $(f \circ g)(x)$ b. $(g \circ f)(x)$

     c. $(f \circ g)(5)$ d. $(g \circ f)(5)$

Solution:

     a. $(f \circ g)(x) = f(g(x))$ we will substitute $g(x)$ for x in $f(x)$

$$= 3(x^2 - 2x + 6) - 4$$

$$= 3x^2 - 6x + 18 - 4$$

$$= 3x^2 - 6x + 14$$

b. $(g \circ f)(x) = g(f(x))$ we will substitute $f(x)$ for x in $g(x)$

$$= (3x - 4)^2 - 2(3x - 4) + 6$$

$$= 9x^2 - 24x + 16 - 6x + 8 + 6$$

$$= 9x^2 - 30x + 30$$

c. $(f \circ g)(5) = f(g(5)) = f(5^2 - 2 * 5 + 6)$

$$= f(21) = 3(21) - 4 = -4$$
$$= 59$$

d. $(g \circ f)(5) =$
$$g(f(5)) = g(3 * 5 - 4)$$

$$= g(11) = 11^2 - 2 * 11 + 6$$

$$= 105$$

A graphing calculator can be used to check both c and d. See Chapter 6, Example 4

Note:

$\underline{f(g(x)) \neq g(f(x))}$

        except in special cases.

Example 5: $f(x) = 2x - 4$ and $g(x) = \sqrt{x}$.

    Find   a. $(f \circ g)(x)$ b. $(g \circ f)(x)$

        c. find the domain of $f \circ g$ and $g \circ f$

Solution:

a. $(f \circ g)(x) = f(g(x)) = 2\sqrt{x} - 4$

b.. $(g \circ f)(x) = g(f(x)) = \sqrt{2x - 4}$

c. The domain of f is $(-\infty, \infty)$ and the domain of g is $[0, \infty)$.
To find the domain of $f \circ g$, look first at the domain of g which is $x \geq 0$. The output from these numbers will be within the domain of f. Since f can input any real number, then any output that comes from g will be okay. Thus all of the domain of g can be input. Thus, the domain of $f \circ g$ is $[0, \infty)$.

To find the domain of $(g \circ f)(x)$, first look at the domain of f which is all real numbers. The outputs from f with all real numbers as inputs will also be all real numbers. These outputs of f will be the inputs for g but these cannot be negative. We will need

$$2x - 4 \geq 0 \quad \text{or} \quad x \geq 2.$$

The domain of $(g \circ f)(x)$ is $[2, \infty)$.

Example 6: Given $f(x) = \dfrac{1}{x+2}$ and $g(x) = \dfrac{4}{x}$, find

    a. $(f \circ g)(x)$ b. $(g \circ f)(x)$

    c. find the domain of $f \circ g$ and $g \circ f$

Solution:

    a. $(f \circ g)(x) = f(g(x)) = \dfrac{1}{\dfrac{4}{x} + 2} = \dfrac{1}{\dfrac{4 + 2x}{x}} = \dfrac{x}{4 + 2x} = \dfrac{x}{2(2 + x)}$

    b. $(g \circ f)(x) = g(f(x)) = \dfrac{4}{\dfrac{1}{x+2}} = 4(x + 2)$

    c. The domain of f is $x \neq -2$ and the domain of g is $x \neq 0$.
When we look for the domain of $f \circ g$, we see that zero is not in the domain of g, so 0 is not in the domain of $f \circ g$.

The domain of f cannot contain -2, so the output of g must not be -2. Solve

$$\frac{4}{x} = -2$$

$$-2x = 4 \qquad \text{or} \qquad x = -2$$

From this calculation, again $x \neq -2$ and the domain of $f \circ g$ would be

$$(-\infty, -2) \cup (-2, 0) \cup (0, \infty)$$

To find the domain of $g \circ f$, we know that from the domain of f $x \neq -2$.

Thus -2 is not in the domain of $g \circ f$

Since the domain of g is $x \neq 0$ then

$$f(x) = 1/x + 2 \text{ cannot equal zero because the numerator is 1.}$$

Thus there is no restriction. The domain of $g \circ f$ is $(-\infty, -2) \cup (-2, \infty)$

Decomposing a Function

When we decompose a function our goal is to try to express the given function as a composition of two functions.

Example 7: If $f(x) = (x-4)^7$, find $g(x)$ and $h(x)$ such that

$$f(x) = (g \circ h)(x)$$

Solution: The best way to approach decomposing a function is to carefully examine the given function and try to find a way to represent it as two functions.

When we examine f, we see that $f(x)$ raises $(x-4)$ to the 7th power.

Two functions that can be used for the composition are:

$$g(x) = x^7 \quad \text{and} \quad h(x) = (x-4).$$

Next, we must check to see if our two functions satisfy the required composition.

Our problem stated that our composition should be

$$f(x) = (g \circ h)(x)$$

$$= g(h(x)) = g(x-4) = (x-4)^7$$

which is our original function given in the problem.

Section 1.5 Exercises

Given: $f(x) = 2x^2$ and $g(x) = 4x + 3$, find the following:

1. $(f + g)(4)$

2. $(f - g)(0)$

3. $(fg)((-\frac{1}{2})$

4. $(fg)(\frac{1}{2})$

5. $(f/g)(\sqrt{2})$

6. $(g/f)(0)$

7. $(g + g)(2)$

8. $(g - f)(-2)$

9. $(f/g)(-2)$

10. $(f + g)(-\frac{1}{4})$

For each pair of functions below find:
$(f+g)(x)$, $(f-g)(x)$, $(fg)(x)$, $(ff)(x)$, $(f/g)(x)$, $(gg)(x)$ and $(g/f)(x)$?

11. $f(x) = 3x - 2$; $g(x) = 4 - 2x$

12. $f(x) = 2x - 3$ $g(x) = x^2 + 3$

13. $f(x) = \sqrt{x+1}$ $g(x) = x - 2$

14. $f(x) = \sqrt{x}$ $g(x) = x^2$

15. $f(x) = |x|$ $g(x) = x - 2$

16. $f(x) = \dfrac{2}{x-1}$ $g(x) = \dfrac{1}{2-x}$

For each function f, find and simplify the difference quotient:

$$\frac{f(x+h) - f(x)}{h}$$

17. $f(x) = 2x^2 - 1$

18. $f(x) = 4 - 2x$

19. $f(x) = 3x^2 + 4x - 5$

20. $f(x) = 2x^3 - 4x^2$

Given that $f(x) = 4x - 1$ and $g(x) = x^2 - x - 6$, find the following:

21. $(f \circ g)(-2)$

22. $(g \circ f)(-1)$

23. $(f \circ g)(0)$

24. $(f \circ f)(2)$

Find $(f \circ g), (g \circ f)$ and the domain of each:

25. Given $f(x) = x + 4$ and $g(x) = x - 2$

26. Given $f(x) = \dfrac{1}{x}$ and $g(x) = x$

Find $f(x)$ and $g(x)$ if $h(x) = (f \circ g)(x)$

27. $h(x) = (7 - x)^3$

28. $h(x) = \dfrac{1}{(x - 3)^6}$

29. $h(x) = (\sqrt{x} - 4)^2$

30. $h(x) = \sqrt[4]{(x - 2)^3}$

Section 1.6 Transformations

Symmetry: A graph is symmetric if there is an axis or a point that can be drawn so that the graph will mirror itself across this axis or point.

If the coordinate plane is folded along the *y*-axis, and if the graph that lies on the left half of the plane coincides with the graph on the right, then the graph is **symmetric with respect to the *y*-axis.**

A graph is **symmetric with respect to the *y*-axis** provided that the point $(-x, y)$ is on the graph whenever the point (x, y) is on the graph.

Points that have the same *y*-value and opposite *x*-values are **reflections of each other across the *y*-axis.**

The points $(4, 1)$ and $(-4, 1)$ are reflections across the *y*-axis.

A graph is **symmetric with respect to the *x*-axis** provided that the point $(x, -y)$ is on the graph whenever the point (x, y) is on the graph.

When the graph is folded along the *x*-axis, points above and below the *x*-axis coincide.

A graph **is symmetric with respect to the origin** provided that the point $(-x, -y)$ is on the graph whenever the point (x, y) is on the graph.

Rather than folding the graph along either axis, we can see reflection across the origin by rotating the graph 180° and the result will coincide with the original figure.

Given the point $(5, -2)$, its reflection across the origin would be the point $(-5, 2)$.

Tests for symmetry:

x-axis: Replace y with $-y$. Simplify. If the result is the same as the original equation, then the graph is symmetric with respect to the *x*-axis.

y-axis: Replace x with $-x$. Simplify. If the result is the same as the original equation, then the graph is symmetric with respect to the *y*-axis.

origin: Replace x with $-x$ and y with $-y$. Simplify. If the result is the same as the original equation, then the graph is symmetric with respect to the origin.

Example 1. Find if $x^2 + y^2 = 9$ is symmetric to the *x*-axis, the *y*-axis and the origin.

Solution:

1. Test for symmetry to the *x*-axis: replace y with $-y$

$x^2 + y^2 = 9$ given equation

$x^2 + (-y)^2 = 9$ substitute and simplify

$x^2 + y^2 = 9$

    The resulting equation is the same as the original so the graph is symmetric to the *x*-axis.

2. Test for symmetry to the *y*-axis: replace x with $-x$

$x^2 + y^2 = 9$ given equation

$(-x)^2 + y^2 = 9$ substitute and simplify

$x^2 + y^2 = 9$

    The resulting equation is the same as the original so the graph is symmetric to the *y*-axis.

3. Test for symmetry to the origin: replace x with $-x$ and y with $-y$

$x^2 + y^2 = 9$ given equation

$(-x)^2 + (-y)^2 = 9$ substitute and simplify

$x^2 + y^2 = 9$

    The resulting equation is the same as the original so the graph is symmetric to the origin.

This problem can be solved using a graphing calculator. To see this problem, see Chapter 6, Example 5.

Example 2

Find if $y = x^2 + 4$ is symmetric to the x-axis, the y-axis and the origin.

Solution:

1. Test for symmetry to the x-axis: replace y with $-y$:

$$y = x^2 + 4 \qquad \text{given equation}$$
$$(-y) = x^2 + 4 \qquad \text{substitute and simplify}$$
$$-y = x^2 + 4$$

The resulting equation is not the same as the original equation. Thus the graph is not symmetric with respect to the x-axis.

2. Test for symmetry to the y-axis   replace x with $-x$

$$y = x^2 + 4 \qquad \text{given equation}$$
$$y = (-x)^2 + 4 \qquad \text{substitute and simplify}$$
$$y = x^2 + 4$$

The resulting equation is the same as the original equation so the graph is symmetric to the y-axis

3. Test for symmetry to the origin: replace x with $-x$ and y with $-y$:

$$y = x^2 + 4 \qquad \text{given equation}$$
$$(-y) = (-x)^2 + 4 \qquad \text{substitute and simplify}$$
$$-y = x^2 + 4$$

The resulting equation is not the same as the original equation. Thus the graph is not symmetric with respect to the origin.

This example can be solved using a graphing calculator. See Chapter 6, Example 6.

Even and Odd Functions:

> **Even and Odd Functions:**
> An even function is a function that is symmetric with respect to the y-axis.
> or $f(x) = f(-x)$ for every x in the domain of f.
> An odd function is a function that is symmetric with respect to the origin.
> or $f(-x) = -f(x)$ for every x in the domain of f.

A function cannot be both even and odd except for the function $f(x) = 0$.

How to test for even/odd function:

Given a function $f(x)$

1. Find $f(-x)$ by replacing x with $-x$ in the function. Simplify. If $f(x) = f(-x)$, then the given function is even.

2. Find $-f(x)$ by multiplying the function by -1. Simplify. If $f(-x) = -f(x)$ then the given function is odd.

Example 3: Are the given functions even, odd or neither?

    a. $f(x) = 2x^5 - x^3 + 4x$ b. $f(x) = 4x^4 + x^2$

Solution:

    a. $f(x) = 2x^5 - x^3 + 4x$

    1. $f(-x) = 2(-x)^5 - (-x)^3 + 4(-x)$

         $f(-x) = -2x^5 + x^3 - 4x$

We see that $\quad f(x) \neq f(-x) \quad$ and the function is not even

    2. $-f(x) = -(2x^5 - x^3 + 4x)$

         $-f(x) = -2x^5 + x^3 - 4x$

We see that $f(-x) = -f(x)$ and the function is odd.

    .b. $f(x) = 4x^4 + x^2$

         $f(-x) = 4(-x)^4 + (-x)^2$

         $f(-x) = 4x^4 + x^2$

We see that $\quad f(x) = f(-x) \quad$ and the function is even.

See Chapter 6, Example 7 for this example solved with a graphing calculator.

Transformations of Functions:

We need to be able to recognize certain graphs and the functions they represent. Several common functions are shown below:

Identity function: $f(x) = x$

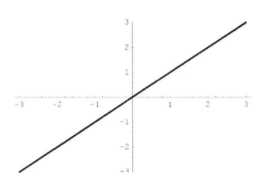

Square function: $f(x) = x^2$

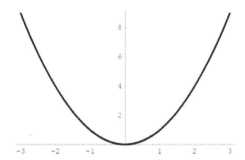

Square root function: $f(x) = \sqrt{x}$

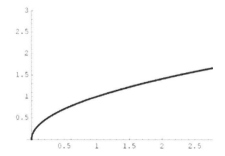

Cube function: $f(x) = x^3$

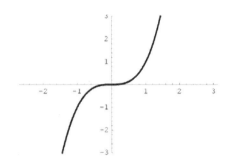

Reciprocal function: $f(x) = \dfrac{1}{x}$

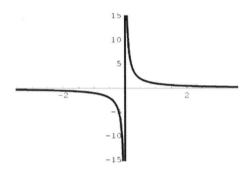

Absolute value function: $f(x) = |x|$

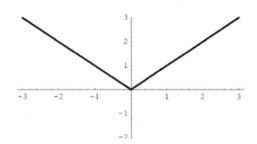

Transformations: horizontal, vertical, stretching, shrinking and reflecting across axis of functions.

Next we will learn how to shift these basic functions.

Vertical Translations:

> **Vertical Translation: For any function $f(x)$ and for any $c \neq 0$,**
>
>   **Graph of $y = f(x) + c$ is the graph of $y = f(x)$ shifted _up c units_,**
>
>   **Graph of $y = f(x) - c$ is the graph of $y = f(x)$ shifted _down c units_.**

Example 4. The function $f(x) = x^2 + 4$ is the graph of $f(x) = x^2$ shifted up 4 units.

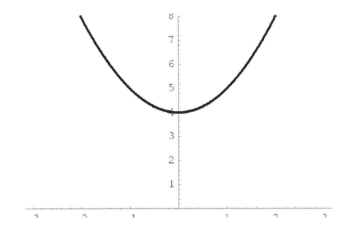

and the function $f(x) = x^2 - 3$ is the graph of $f(x) = x^2$ shifted down 3 units

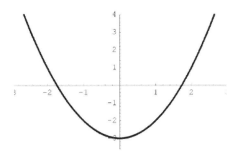

Horizontal Translations:

> **Horizontal Translation:** For any function $f(x)$ and for any $c \neq 0$,
>
> Graph of $y = f(x - c)$ is the graph of $y = f(x)$ shifted *right c units*,
>
> Graph of $y = f(x + c)$ is the graph of $y = f(x)$ shifted *left c units*.

Example 5 The graph of $f(x-2)^2$ is the graph of $f(x) = x^2$ **shifted right 2 units**

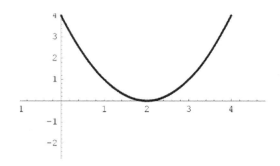

and the graph of $f(x+3)^2$ is the graph of $f(x) = x^2$ **shifted left 3 units**

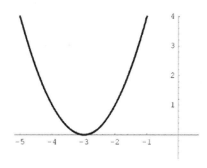

Example 6: For each of the given, describe how each graph can be obtained from one of the basic graphs shown earlier.

a. $h(x) = x^2 - 4$ b. $h(x) = (x-3)^2$

c. $h(x) = |x| + 2$ d. $h(x) = |x - 2|$

e. $h(x) = x^3 + 1$ f. $h(x) = (x-3)^3$

Solution:

a. $h(x) = x^2 - 4$ is a shift of the graph $f(x) = x^2$ (the square function) down 4 units. Or, we can say that $h(x)$ is the graph of $f(x)$ translated down 4 units. This is a vertical translation.

b. $h(x) = (x - 3)^2$ is a shift of the graph $f(x) = x^2$ (the square function) right 3 units. Or, we can say that $h(x)$ is the graph of $f(x)$ translated right 3 units. This is a horizontal translation

c. $h(x) = |x| + 2$ is a shift of the graph $f(x) = |x|$ (the absolute function) up 2 units. Or, we can say that $h(x)$ is the graph of $f(x)$ translated up 2 units. This is a vertical translation.

d. $h(x) = |x - 2|$ is a shift of the graph $f(x) = |x|$ (the absolute function) right 2 units. Or, we can say that $h(x)$ is the graph of $f(x)$ translated right 2 units. This is a horizontal translation.

e. $h(x) = x^3 + 1$ is a shift of the graph $f(x) = x^3$ (the cube function) up 1 unit. Or, we can say that $h(x)$ is the graph of $f(x)$ translated up 1 unit. This is a vertical translation.

f. $h(x) = (x - 3)^3$ is a shift of the graph $f(x) = x^3$ (the cube function) right 3 units. Or, we can say that $h(x)$ is the graph of $f(x)$ translated right 3 units. This is a horizontal translation.

This example can be solved using the graphing calculator to get a view of the graph and its translation. See Chapter 6, Example 8.

Reflections

Graphs can be reflected across the *x*-axis and the *y*-axis. When a graph is reflected, the new graph is called a reflection.

To reflect *f*(*x*) across the *x*-axis,
  graph $-f(x)$
To reflect *f*(*x*) across the *y*-axis,
  graph $f(-x)$
If a point (*x*,*y*) is on the graph of *f*(*x*),
  then $(x, -y)$ is on the graph $y = -f(x)$
  and $(-x, y)$ is on the graph $y = f(-x)$

If $f(x) = x^2$ the graph is:

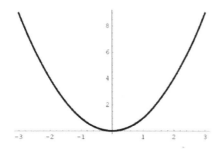

then $g(x) = -f(x)$ reflects across the x-axis:

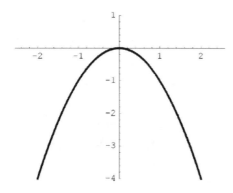

If $f(x) = x^3$, the graph is:

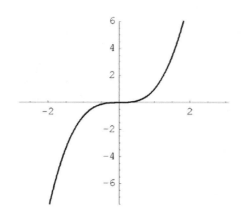

64

then $g(x) = f(-x)$ reflects across the y-axis:

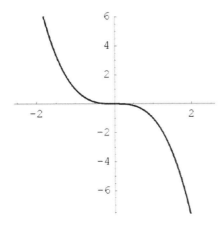

Example 7: If a function $f(x)$ is defined as $f(x) = 2x^3 - 3x$, describe what the new function will look like

$$g(x) = 2(-x)^3 - 3(-x)$$

Solution:

If we compare $f(x)$ and $g(x)$, we see that in the new function $g(x)$ the variable x has been replaced with $-x$. Thus $g(x) = 2(-x)^3 - 3(-x)$ is a reflection of the function f across the y-axis.

Vertical Stretching and Shrinking

To obtain the graph $y = cf(x)$ for some real number c, we <u>multiply the y-coordinates</u> of the points on the graph of $y = f(x)$ by c.

For example if $y = 3f(x)$, we would multiply each y-coordinate by 3; If $y = \dfrac{1}{3}f(x)$, we multiply each y-coordinate by ⅓,

This process is referred to as **vertically stretching** the graph of f if $|c|$ is > 1, or **vertically shrinking** the graph when $0 < |c| < 1$.

65

Given the function $y = f(x)$.

    $y = cf(x)$ if $\left| c \right| > 1$ then the graph of f is **vertically stretched** by a factor of c

       if $0 < \left| c \right| < 1$ then the graph of f is **vertically shrunk** by a factor of c

Horizontal Stretching and Shrinking

To obtain the graph $y = f(cx)$ for some real number c, we <u>divide the x-coordinates</u> of the points on the graph of $y = f(x)$ by c.

This process is referred to as **horizontally shrinking** the graph of f for $\left| c \right| > 1$, or **horizontally stretching** the graph when $0 < \left| c \right| < 1$.

Given the function
    $y = f(x)$

    $y = f(cx)$ if $\left| c \right| > 1$
        then the graph of f is **horizontally shrunk** by a factor of $1/c$

      if $0 < \left| c \right| < 1$
        then the graph of f is **horizontally stretched** by a factor of $1/c$

Example 8:

    Given $y = f(x)$ for some function f. Describe what changes occur to the graph of f with each of the following:

    a. $g(x) = 3f(x)$ b. $g(x) = \frac{1}{3}f(x)$ c. $g(x) = f(4x)$
    d. $g(x) = f(\frac{1}{8}x)$ e. $g(x) = -f(x)$ f. $g(x) = f(-x)$

Solution:
    a. $g(x) = 3f(x)$: this graph is of the form $cf(x)$, and we know that this is a vertical change. Since $\left| 3 \right| > 1$, we know this is a stretch. Thus, $g(x)$ is a vertical stretching of the graph of f by a factor of 3.

66

b. $g(x) = \frac{1}{3}f(x)$: this graph is of the form $cf(x)$, and we know that this is a vertical change. Since $0 < \left|\frac{1}{3}\right| < 1$, we know this is a shrinking. Thus, $g(x)$ is a vertical shrinking of the graph of f by a factor of $\frac{1}{3}$.

c. $g(x) = f(4x)$: this graph is of the form $f(cx)$, and we know this is a horizontal change. Since $\left|4\right| > 1$, we know this is a horizontal shrink. Thus, $g(x)$ is a horizontal shrinking of the graph of f by a factor of $1/4$.

d. $g(x) = f(\frac{1}{8}x)$: this graph is of the form $f(cx)$, and we know this is a horizontal change. Since $\left|1/8\right| < 1$, we know this is a horizontal stretching. . Thus, $g(x)$ is a horizontal stretching of the graph of f by a factor of 8.

e. $g(x) = -f(x)$: this is a reflection and $g(x)$ is a reflection across the x-axis

f. $g(x) = f(-x)$: this is a reflection and $g(x)$ is a reflection across the y-axisThe table below is a table describing transformations and their results.

TRANSFORMATIONS of $y = f(x)$:

Vertical Translation: $y = f(x) +$ or $-c$

     $y = f(x) + c$ is the graph of f **shifted up c units**
     $y = f(x) - c$ is the graph of f **shifted down c units**

Horizontal Translation: $y = f(x +$ or $-c)$

     $y = f(x + c)$ is the graph of f shifted **left c units**
     $y = f(x - c)$ is the graph of f shifted **right c units**

Vertical Stretching or Shrinking : $y = cf(x)$

     For $\left|c\right| > 1$ a **vertical stretch**
       $0 < \left|c\right| < 1$ **a vertical shrink**

Horizontal Stretching or Shrinking: $y = f(cx)$

     For $\left|c\right| > 1$ **a horizontal shrink**
       $0 < \left|c\right| < 1$ **a horizontal stretch**

Reflections:

     $y = -f(x)$ is a reflection of f **across the x-axis**
     $y = f(-x)$ is a reflection of f **across the y-axis**

Exercises 1.6

Draw the graph of a function that is:

      1 symmetric with respect to the x-axis
      2. symmetric with respect to the y-axis
      3. symmetric with respect to the origin

Determine whether the given equations are symmetric with respect to the x-axis, the y-axis, the origin, or none:

4. $y = |x| + 3$ 5. $y = |x|$

6. $y = |x + 2|$ 7. $4y = 2x + 6$

8. $2x + 3 = 2y$ 9. $3y = x^2 - 4$

10. $x^2 + 1 = 4y$ 11. $y = 4$

12. $y = \dfrac{2}{x}$ 13. $y = -2x^3$

Find the point that is symmetric to the given point with respect to the x-axis, the y-axis, the origin:

14. $(-4, 3)$ 15. $(1/2, 0)$
16. $(-2, -3)$ 17. $(2, \frac{1}{3})$
18. $(0, -2)$ 19. $(5, -4)$

Determine algebraically whether the function is even, odd, or neither.

20. $f(x) = 4x^3$ 21. $f(x) = 4x^3 + 3$
22. $f(x) = x^5$ 23. $f(x) = x^6$

24. $f(x) = \sqrt[3]{x}$ 25. $f(x) = \dfrac{1}{x}$

26. $f(x) = \dfrac{1}{2x^2}$ 27. $f(x) = \sqrt{x + 2}$

For each of the given, describe how each graph can be obtained from the graph of $f(x) = x^2$.

28. $f(x) = x^2 + 2$ 29. $f(x) = -x^2$
30. $f(x) = x^2 - 3$ 31. $f(x) = (x + 2)^2$
32. $f(x) = (x - 4)^2$ 33. $f(x) = 3x^2$
34. $f(x) = -(x + 3)^2$ 35. $f(x) = (x - 4)^2 - 3$

Chapter 1 Summary

Functions

Each member of domain corresponds to **<u>exactly</u>** one member of the range.

Domain: input values
Range: output values

Test for function: Vertical Line Test

Slopes/Lines

Slope: $$m = \frac{y_2 - y_1}{x_2 - x_1}$$

Slope-Intercept Equation:
$$y = mx + b$$

Point-Slope Equation:
$$y - y_1 = m(x - x_1)$$

Horizontal Line: $y = b$

Vertical Line: $x = a$

Parallel Lines: $m_1 = m_2. \quad b_1 \neq b_2$

Perpendicular Lines:
$$m_1\, m_2 = -1 \quad \text{or}$$
vertical and horizontal lines

Algebra for Fractions

Sum: $(f + g)(x) = f(x) + g(x)$

Difference: $(f - g)(x) = f(x) - g(x)$

Product: $(fg)(x) = f(x) * g(x)$

Quotient: $(f / g)(x) = f(x) / g(x), \; g(x) \neq 0$

Composition: $(f \circ g)(x) = f(g(x))$
$(g \circ f)(x) = g(f(x))$

Symmetry Tests

x-axis: replace y with $-y$, get equivalent equation

y-axis: replace x with $-x$, get equivalent equation

origin: replace x with $-x$ and replace y with $-y$ and get an equivalent equation

Transformations

Vertical Translation:	$y = f(x) \pm c$
Horizontal Translation:	$y = g(x \pm c)$
Reflection across x-axis	$y = -f(x)$
Reflection across y-axis	$y = f(-x)$
Horizontal Stretching/Shrinking	$y = f(cx)$
Vertical Stretching/Shrinking	$y = cf(x)$

Chapter 1 Review:

Is the given relation a function? Find the domain and range:
1. {(2,3),(4,5),(6,5),(2,7)
2. {(2,4),(2,5),(2,6),(2,7)}

Is the given graph a function:
3.

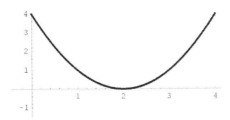

4.

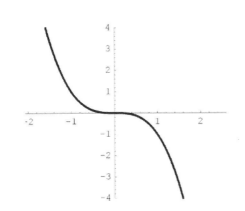

5.

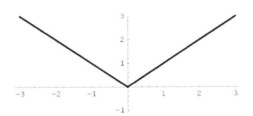

Find the domain of the following:

6. $f(x) = 5x - 3x^2$

7. $f(x) = \dfrac{2}{x}$

8. $f(x) = \dfrac{2}{x^2 - x - 6}$

9. $|x - 4|$

Given the function $f(x) = x^2 - 2x + 1$, find
10. $f(2)$

11. $f(-2)$

12. $f(y+2)$

13. $f(0)$

Find the slope of the line containing the given points:

71

14. $(2, -3), (4, -1)$ 15. $(1, 3),(7, 3)$

16. $(2, 5),(2, 4)$ 17. $(1/3, 2/3),(-1/8, 5/8)$

18. Find the slope and y-intercept:
$$-3x - 2y = 9$$

Write the equation of a line in slope-intercept form for the following:

19. $m = -4$, y-intercept $(0, 3)$

20. $m = -1/3$, y-intercept $(0, 4)$

21. contains the points $(2, -3)$ and $(-1, -1)$

Are the lines parallel, perpendicular or neither:

22. $2x - 3y = 9$ 23. $y - 2x = 4$

     $4x = 6y + 12$ $y = 2x + 6$

24. Find the equation of the line thru $(1, 0)$ and parallel to the line $y - 2x = 4$.

25. Find the equation of the line thru $(2, -4)$ and perpendicular to $y - 2x = 4$.

26. Find the equation of the line thru $(1, -2)$ and parallel to the line $y = 7$.

27. Find the equation of the line thru $(1, -2)$ and perpendicular to the line $y = 7$.

Given $f(x) = \sqrt{x + 2}$ and $g(x) = x^2 - 2$. Find:

28. $(f+g)(2)$ 29. $(f-g)(2)$

30. $(ff)(1)$

31. Find $(f \circ g)(x)$ and $(g \circ f)(x)$ given $f(x) = x^2 + x$ and $g(x) = x - 3$

Determine algebraically whether the given equation is symmetric to the x-axis, the y-axis and the origin:

32. $x^2 + 2y^2 = 1$ 33. $x^2 + y^2 = 9$

34. $x + 2y = 3$ 35. $y = x^2$

36. $y = -x^3$ 37. $y = x^4$

38. $y = |x| + 2$ 39. $y = |x + 2|$

Write an equation for a function that has a graph with:

40. shaped as $y = x^2$ but shifted 4 units down and 3 units left

41. shaped as $y = |x|$ stretched vertically by a factor of 3 and shifted up 2 units.

CHAPTER 2

Equations, Inequalities and Functions

Section 2.1: Linear Equations and Functions

Equation: A statement that two expressions are equal.

To **solve an equation** means to find all numbers that when substituted into the equation in place of the variable make the equation a true statement. A number that is a solution of an equation is said to **satisfy the equation**. All solutions of an equation make up the **solution set of the equation**.

A linear equation in one variable is an equation that can be written in the form:

$ax + b = 0$

where a and b are real numbers with a $\neq$ 0.

We can use the Addition Property and/ or the Subtraction Property of Equality to solve linear equations.

The Addition Property of Equality:

Adding the same number to both sides of an equation does not change the solution to the equation:

If $a = b,$ then $a + c = b + c$

The Subtraction Property of Equality:

Subtracting the same number from both sides of an equation does not change the solution to the equation:

If $a = b,$ then $a - c = b - c$

Example 1: Solve the equation: $x - 3 = 5$

Solution: Given:

$$x - 3 = 5$$
$$x - 3 + 3 = 5 + 3 \qquad \text{Addition Property of Equality}$$
$$x = 8 \qquad \text{Combine like terms}$$

Check:

$$x - 3 = 5$$
$$8 - 3 = 5$$
$$5 = 5 \qquad \textbf{True statement}$$

We will also use the Multiplication and/or Division Property of Equality to solve linear equations.

The Multiplication Property of Equality:
Multiplying both sides of an equation by the same nonzero number does not change the solution to the equation:

$$\text{If} \quad a = b \text{ and } c \neq 0 \quad \text{then} \quad ac = bc$$

The Division Property of Equality:
Dividing both sides of an equation by the same nonzero number does not change the solution to the equation:

$$\text{If} \quad a = b \text{ and } c \neq 0 \quad \textbf{then} \quad \frac{a}{c} = \frac{b}{c}$$

Example 2: Solve $4x - 3 = 2$

Solution: Given

$$4x - 3 = 2$$
$$4x - 3 + 3 = 2 + 3 \qquad \text{Addition Property}$$
$$4x = 5 \qquad \text{Combine like terms}$$
$$\frac{4}{4}x = \frac{5}{4} \qquad \text{Division Property}$$

$$x = \frac{5}{4}$$

Check:

$$4x - 3 = 2$$

$$4\left(\frac{5}{4}\right) - 3 = 2$$
$$5 - 3 = 2$$
$$2 = 2 \qquad \textbf{True statement}$$

We can also solve Example 1 as well as Example 2 using a graphing calculator. See Chapter 6, Example 9.

Example 3. Solve: $2(4 - 2x) = 5 - 3(x + 1)$

Solution: Given : $\qquad 2(4 - 2x) = 5 - 3(x + 1)$

$8 - 4x = 5 - 3x - 3$	Distributive Property
$8 - 4x = 2 - 3x$	Combine like terms
$8 - 4x + 4x = 2 - 3x + 4x$	Addition Property
$8 = 2 + x$	Combine like terms
$8 - 2 = 2 + x - 2$	Addition Property
$6 = x$	

Check:
$$2(4 - 2x) = 5 - 3(x + 1)$$
$$8 - 4x = 5 - 3x - 3$$
$$8 - 4 * 6 = 5 - 3 * 6 - 3$$
$$8 - 24 = 5 - 18 - 3$$
$$-16 = -16 \qquad \textbf{True statement}$$

A graphing calculator can be used to solve this example. See Chapter 6, Example 10.

Zeros of Linear Functions

Real zeros of a function are the input values to the function that will make $f(x) = 0$.

These values are also the x-value of the x-intercepts of the graph.

A linear function is given by $f(x) = ax + b$ where a and b are constants ($a \neq 0$).

76

If we look at the function $f(x) = 2x + 4$, we see that $f(-2) = 2(-2) + 4 = 0$. Thus -2 is a zero of the given function.

A linear function has at most one zero.

If we graph the function $f(x) = 2x + 4$

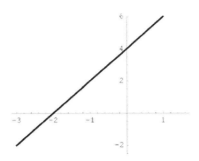

we can see that the zero which is -2 is the x-coordinate of the point where the graph intersects the x-axis.

The x-intercept of the graph is the point $(-2, 0)$.

If we are given a linear function: $f(x) = ax + b$ $(a \neq 0)$ we can set the function equal to zero and find the solution to this equation which will give us the zero of the function.

> **The zero of the function** $f(x) = ax + b$ $(a \neq 0)$ is the solution to the equation $ax + b = 0$.

Example 4. Find the zero of $f(x) = 6x - 3$.

Solution: To find the zeros of a function we find the value of x such that $f(x) = 0$.

Begin by setting $f(x)$ equal to zero.

$$6x - 3 = 0 \qquad \text{Set the function} = 0$$

$$6x = 3 \qquad \text{Add 3 to both sides}$$

$$x = \frac{1}{2} \qquad \text{Divide both sides by 6}$$

Check:
$$f(x) = 6x - 3$$

$$f\left(\frac{1}{2}\right) = 6\left(\frac{1}{2}\right) - 3 = 0$$

$x = \dfrac{1}{2}$ is the **zero of the linear function** since $f\left(\dfrac{1}{2}\right) = 0$

See Chapter 6, Example 11 for the graphic solution to the given problem in Example 4.

Formulas

We can use the same methods that we have used to solve linear equations to solve formulas for a specified variable.

Example 5:   Solve $M = 4t + 3p$ for p.

Solution:

To solve for p we will isolate p:

$$M = 4t + 3p$$
$$M - 4t = 4t + 3p - 4t \qquad \text{Subtract } 4t \text{ from both sides}$$
$$M - 4t = 3p$$
$$\frac{M - 4t}{3} = p \qquad \text{Divide both sides by 3}$$

Example 6:   Solve $T = 6pr + rd$ for r

Solution:

To solve for r we will need to isolate r:

$$T = 6pr + rd$$

$$T = r(6p + d) \qquad \text{Factor out } r$$

$$\frac{T}{6p + d} = r \qquad \text{Divide both sides by } 6p + d$$

Zero of a Function and Solution of an Equation

To find the zero of $f(x)$, set $f(x) = 0$ and solve.

The solution of the equation is the zero of the function.

The zero of $f(x)$ is the x-value of the x-intercept of the graph of $f(x)$.

Section 2.1 Exercises.

Solve.

1. $3x + 3 = 24$ 2. $2t - 4 = 9$

3. $2x - 7 = 0$ 4. $5p = 0$

5. $4 - p = 6$ 6. $5 - 3x = 11$

7. $x + 2 = 2x - 5$ 8. $2 + p = 2p + 1$

9. $5x + 4 = 3x + 10$ 10. $4m - 3 = m + 6$

11. $5x + 4 - 2x = 2x - x + 14$ 12. $8(5x + 3) = 6(2x - 5)$

13. $3(2t - 2) + 6 = 4(t - 2)$ 14. $4(2x + 3) = 6(2x - 1)$

Find the zero of the linear function.

15. $f(x) = x + 3$ 16. $f(x) = 4x + 8$

17. $f(x) = 5 - x$ 18. $f(x) = 3x + 12$

19. $f(x) = 7 - 3x$ 20. $f(x) = 6 - x$

Solve.

21. $A = \dfrac{1}{2}bh$ for h 22. $A = \dfrac{1}{2}bh$ for b

23. $y = mx + b$ for b 24. $y = mx + b$ for m

25. $P = 2L + 2W$ for L 26. $P = 2L + 2W$ for W

27. $T = pcd + de$ for d 28. $T = pcd + de$ for e

29. $2x + 3y = 6$ for x 30. $2x + 3y = 6$ for y

31. $m = n + nde$ for n 32. $t = v - wv$ for v

Section 2.2 Complex Numbers

To solve the equation $x^2 + 1 = 0$, we see that $x^2 = -1$ or $x = \pm\sqrt{-1}$. But $\sqrt{-1}$ has no meaning since there is no real number that when multiplied by itself will result in -1.

However, there is an extension of the number system, called **complex numbers**, in which $x^2 = -1$ does have two solutions.

Complex numbers are formed by adding the imaginary unit i to the real number system.

Definition of i:

$$i = \sqrt{-1} \qquad \text{and} \qquad i^2 = -1$$

The set of complex numbers is the set of all numbers of the form

$$a + bi$$

where a and b are real numbers, $i = \sqrt{-1}$ and $i^2 = -1$

Imaginary Numbers:

In the **complex number _a + bi_,**

_a_ is called the real part of the number and

_bi_ is called the imaginary part. If $b \neq 0$

The number _bi_ is called an imaginary number.

Example 1: Rewrite each of the given in terms of i

    a. $\sqrt{-6}$ b. $\sqrt{-25}$ c. $-\sqrt{-10}$

    d. $-\sqrt{-49}$ e. $\sqrt{-32}$

Solution:

    a. $\sqrt{-6} = \sqrt{-1*6} = \sqrt{-1} * \sqrt{6} = i\sqrt{6}$ or $\sqrt{6}\, i$

    b. $\sqrt{-25} = \sqrt{-1*25} = \sqrt{-1} * \sqrt{25} = 5i$

    c. $-\sqrt{-10} = -\sqrt{-1*10} = -\sqrt{-1} * \sqrt{10} = -i\sqrt{10}$ or $-\sqrt{10}\, i$
    d. $-\sqrt{-49} = -\sqrt{-1*49} = -\sqrt{-1} * \sqrt{49} = -i*7 = -7i$

    e. $\sqrt{-32} = \sqrt{-1*32} = \sqrt{-1}*\sqrt{32} = i\sqrt{16*2} = i*4\sqrt{2} = 4i\sqrt{2}$ or $4\sqrt{2}\, i$

Let's look at the graph of the function $f(x) = x^2 + 1$

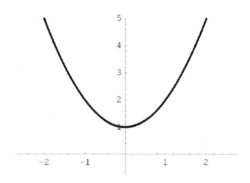

This graph <u>does not cross</u> the x-axis and thus does not have any x-intercepts.

There are no real zeros, and thus there are no real-number solutions to the corresponding equation

$$x^2 + 1 = 0.$$

Addition and Subtraction of Complex Numbers

Complex numbers follow the commutative, associative and distributive rules. We can add and subtract complex numbers just as we do binomials. We collect the real parts together and the imaginary parts together in the same way that we collect like terms in binomials.

Addition:	$(a + bi) + (c + di) = (a + c) + (b + d)i$
Subtraction:	$(a + bi) - (c + di) = (a - c) + (b - d)i$

Example 2. Add, subtract and simply as needed.

a. $(7 + 4i) + (9 + 5i)$ b. $(6 + 3i) - (8 - 6i)$

Solution:

a. $(7 + 4i) + (9 + 5i) = 7 + 4i + 9 + 5i = 7 + 9 + 4i + 5i = 16 + 9i$

b. $(6 + 3i) - (8 - 6i) = 6 + 3i - 8 + 6i = 6 - 8 + 3i + 6i = -2 + 9i$

The preceding problem can be solved using a graphing calculator. See Chapter 6, Example 12.

Multiplication of Complex Numbers

When multiplying imaginary numbers, we must convert them into their imaginary form using i before multiplying.

We must also remember that $i^2 = -1$.

$$\sqrt{-3} * \sqrt{-5} = \sqrt{-1} * \sqrt{3} * \sqrt{-1} * \sqrt{5}$$

$$= i\sqrt{3} * i\sqrt{5} = i^2 \sqrt{15} = -1\sqrt{15} = -\sqrt{15}$$

Multiplication:

> **Two imaginary numbers:** $(bi)(di) = bdi^2 = bd(-1) = -bd$
>
> **Two complex numbers:** $(a + bi)(c + di) = (ac - bd) + (ad + bc)i$

Example 3. Multiply and simplify each of the following

    a. $\sqrt{-9} * \sqrt{-100}$ b. $\sqrt{-49} * \sqrt{-1}$

Solution:

    a.
$$
\begin{aligned}
\sqrt{-9} * \sqrt{-100} &= \sqrt{-1} * \sqrt{9} * \sqrt{-1} * \sqrt{100} \\
&= i * 3 * i * 10 \\
&= i^2 * 30 \\
&= -1 * 30 \\
&= -30
\end{aligned}
$$

    b.
$$
\begin{aligned}
\sqrt{-49} * \sqrt{-1} &= \sqrt{-1} * \sqrt{49} * \sqrt{-1} * \sqrt{1} \\
&= i * 7 * i * 1 \\
&= i^2 * 7 \\
&= (-1) * 7 \\
&= -7
\end{aligned}
$$

Example 4. Multiply and simplify each of the following

    a. $(1 - 3i)(1 + 2i)$ b. $(4 - 2i)^2$

Solution:

    a.
$$
\begin{aligned}
(1 - 3i)(1 + 2i) &= 1 + 2i - 3i - 6i^2 &&\text{Use foil} \\
&= 1 - i - 6(-1) &&i^2 = -1 \\
&= 1 - i + 6 = 7 - i
\end{aligned}
$$

    b.
$$
\begin{aligned}
(4 - 2i)^2 &= (4 - 2i)(4 - 2i) &&\text{Use foil} \\
&= 16 - 8i - 8i + 4i^2 \\
&= 16 - 16i + 4(-1) &&i^2 = -1 \\
&= 16 - 16i - 4 \\
&= 12 - 16i
\end{aligned}
$$

We can use a graphing calculator to multiply complex numbers. See Chapter 6, Example 13.

Simplification of Powers of i

> **Reminder:**
> $$i = \sqrt{-1}$$
> $$i^2 = -1$$
> $$i^3 = i^2 * i = (-1)i = -i$$
> $$i^4 = (i^2)^2 = (-1)^2 = 1$$

The values of the powers of i cycle through the values $\sqrt{-1}, -1, -i,$ and 1

> **To find the values of i raised to any power:**
> 1. Divide the exponent by 4.
> 2. Set the value equal to i raised to the power of the remainder.
> 3. The original value is equal to the value of this new power of i.

Example 5: Simplify each of the following:

    a. i^{25} b. i^{38} c. i^{51} d. i^{60}

Solution:

    a. Simplify i^{25}:   25 divided by 4 = 6 with remainder of 1

$$i^{25} = i^1 = i$$

    b. Simplify i^{38} 38 divided by 4 = 9 with remainder of 2

$$i^{38} = i^2 = -1$$

c. Simplify i^{51} 51 divided by 4 = 12 with remainder of 3

$$i^{51} = i^3 = -i$$

d. Simplify i^{60} 60 divided by 4 = 15 with remainder of zero

$$i^{60} = i^0 = 1$$

Conjugate of a Complex Number

Definition of the Conjugate of a Complex Number:

If $a+bi$ is a complex number, then its conjugate is $a-bi$.

Examples:

Complex Number	Conjugate
$4+3i$	$4-3i$
$6-2i$	$6+2i$
$5i$	$-5i$
4	4

Properties of Conjugates of Complex Numbers:

$$(a+bi)+(a-bi)=2a$$

$$(a+bi)(a-bi)=a^2+b^2$$

Example 6: Multiply the following:

    a. $(4+2i)(4-2i)$ b. $(3i)(-3i)$

Solution:

    a. $(4+2i)(4-2i) = (4)^2 + (2)^2 = 20$

    b. $(3i)(-3i) = -9i^2 = -9(-1) = 9$

$$\frac{a+bi}{c+di} \rightarrow \frac{a+bi}{c+di} * \frac{c-di}{c-di} = \frac{(ac+bd)+(bc-ad)i}{c^2+d^2}$$

$$= \frac{ac+bd}{c^2+d^2} + \frac{(bc-ad)}{c^2+d^2}i$$

Division of Complex Numbers

Think of division as simplifying the quotient of two complex numbers. We can think of this type of simplification as **rationalizing the denominator,** since we are multiplying the both the numerator and denominator of the given quotient by the conjugate of the denominator.

Example 7. Express in the form $a+bi$, where a and b are real numbers

    a. $\dfrac{1}{4+3i}$ b. $\dfrac{2-i}{3-4i}$

Solution:

    a. $\dfrac{1}{4+3i} = \dfrac{1}{4+3i} * \dfrac{4-3i}{4-3i} = \dfrac{4-3i}{16+9} = \dfrac{4}{25} - \dfrac{3}{25}i$

    b. $\dfrac{2-i}{3-4i} = \dfrac{2-i}{3-4i} * \dfrac{3+4i}{3+4i} = \dfrac{6+8i-3i-4i^2}{9+16} = \dfrac{10}{25} + \dfrac{5}{25}i = \dfrac{2}{5} + \dfrac{1}{5}i$

To divide complex numbers using a graphing calculator, see Chapter 6, Example 14.

Section 2.2 Exercises

Simplify and write each answer in $a+bi$ form where a and b are real numbers.

1. $(4+3i)+(6+2i)$

2. $(-2+4i)+(5+3i)$

3. $(-3-2i)+(4+4i)$

4. $(-8+i)+(2i-1)$

5. $(-4-i)+(-2-i)$

6. $(4+\sqrt{-4})+(5-\sqrt{-9})$

7. $(3-\sqrt{-16})+(2+\sqrt{-4})$

8. $(4-3i)-(2+2i)$

9. $(12+7i)-(6-i)$

10. $(3-2i)-(5-4i)$

11. $(-4-2i)-(-3-i)$

12. $(-4-3i)-(-3-4i)$

13. $2i(3-4i)$

14. $2i(6i-4)$

15. $-4i(-6+2i)$

16. $-5i(-2-3i)$

17. $(2+3i)(1+4i)$

18. $(3i+1)(2i+5)$

19. $(3-4i)(2-6i)$

20. $(4-3i)(2-5i)$

21. $(-2-3i)(-5-i)$

22. $(-3-2i)(-4+2i)$

23. $(4-\sqrt{-9})(5+\sqrt{-36}$

24. $(3-\sqrt{-25})(2-\sqrt{-16})$

25. $(3+2i)^2$

26. $(2-4i)^2$

27. $\dfrac{5-2i}{2+3i}$

28. $\dfrac{4-i}{2-i}$

29. $\dfrac{1+i}{1-i}$

30. $\dfrac{4-2i}{5+i}$

Simplify:

31. i^{31}

32. i^{18}

33. i^{68}

34. i^{101}

88

Section 2.3 Quadratic Equations and Functions

An equation that can be written in the form

$$ax^2 + bx + c = 0$$

where *a, b,* and *c* are real numbers with a $\neq$ 0 is a **quadratic equation**.

An equation with an x^2 term as the highest degreed term is called quadratic.

A quadratic equation written in the form $ax^2 + bx + c = 0$ is in standard form.

A function that can be written in the form

$$f(x) = ax^2 + bx + c$$

where *a, b,* and *c* are real numbers with a $\neq$ 0 is a **quadratic function**.

The zeros of a quadratic function $f(x) = ax^2 + bx + c$ are the solutions of the associated quadratic equation $ax^2 + bx + c = 0$. These solutions can also be called **roots** of the equation.

Quadratic functions can have real-number or imaginary-number zeros and quadratic equations can have real-number or imaginary-number solutions.

If the zeros of a quadratic function are real numbers, they are also the first coordinate of the *x*-intercepts of the graph of the quadratic function.

Methods for solving quadratic equations:

1. **Factor method.** The equation is rewritten so that one side equals zero and then factored. The factors are set equal to zero and solved. The results are the solutions to the quadratic equation.

2. **Square root method.** This method is used when the middle term equals zero. The x^2 term is isolated and then the square root is taken of both sides of the equation.

3. **Complete the Square Method.**

4. **Quadratic Formula.**

Example 1. Solve: $x^2 - 3x + 2 = 0$

Solution. Given
$$x^2 - 3x + 2 = 0$$
$$(x - 2)(x - 1) = 0 \qquad \text{Factor}$$
$$x - 2 = 0 \text{ or } x - 1 = 0 \qquad \text{Set each factor } = \text{zero}$$
$$x = 2 \qquad \text{or } x = 1 \qquad \text{Solve}$$

Check: $x = 2$: $(2)^2 - 3(2) + 2 = 0$
$$4 - 6 + 2 = 0$$
$$0 = 0 \qquad \text{True statement}$$

$x = 1$: $(1)^2 - 3(1) + 2 = 0$
$$1 - 3 + 2 = 0$$
$$0 = 0 \qquad \text{True statement}$$

This equation can be solved using a graphing calculator. See Chapter 6, Example 15.

Example 2. Solve $3x^2 - 15 = 0$

Solution: Given

$$3x^2 - 15 = 0 \qquad \text{Use Square Root method since there is not a middle term.}$$
$$3x^2 = 15 \qquad \text{Isolate } x^2.$$
$$x^2 = 5 \qquad \text{Divide both sides by 3.}$$
$$x = \sqrt{5} \qquad \text{or} \qquad x = -\sqrt{5} \qquad \text{Take square root of both sides.}$$

Check: $x = \sqrt{5}$ $3(\sqrt{5})^2 - 15 = 0$

$3 * 5 - 15 = 0$

$0 = 0$ True

$x = -\sqrt{5}$ $3(-\sqrt{5})^2 - 15 = 0$

$3 * 5 - 15 = 0$

$0 = 0$ True

Homework Chapter 1 Review 31,35,41
2.1, 13,19,25
2.2 13,33

A quadratic equation can have two real-number solutions, one real-number solution or two complex-number solutions.

Example 3.   Solve $x^2 + 6 = 0$

Solution: We will solve this equation using the square root method since the equation does not contain a middle term.

$x^2 + 6 = 0$

$x^2 = -6$ Isolate the x^2 term

$x = \pm\sqrt{-6}$ Take the square root of both sides

$x = \pm i\sqrt{6}$

The solutions are imaginary numbers instead of real-numbers and the graph has no x-intercepts.

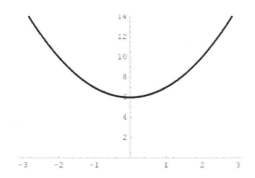

Note: the graph **does not** cross the x-axis.

Completing the Square Method:

> Any quadratic equation can be solved using the square root property if it is first written in the form:
> $$(x + n)^2 = k$$
> for suitable numbers n and k.
>
> Complete the square to get a quadratic equation into this form.

Example 4: Solve $9x^2 - 12x - 1 = 0$

Solution: We need to find constants n and k so that the given equation can be written in the form $(x + n)^2 = k$. If we expand $(x + n)^2$ we find $x^2 + 2xn + n^2$, and the coefficient of x^2 is 1.

Step1: **Get a leading coefficient of 1** in the given equation.

We will multiply both sides of the equation by 1/9:

$$x^2 - \frac{4}{3}x - \frac{1}{9} = 0$$

Step 2: **Move the constant** $-\frac{1}{9}$ to the other side of the equation by adding $\frac{1}{9}$ to both sides of the equation:

$$x^2 - \frac{4}{3}x = \frac{1}{9}$$

Step 3. **Find a number that will make the left side a perfect square**.

To find that number we take $\frac{1}{2}$ of the coefficient of the x-term.

$$\frac{1}{2} * (-\frac{4}{3}) \quad = \quad -\frac{2}{3}$$

92

Step 4: **Square the new number and add this to both sides** of the equation:

$$\left(-\frac{2}{3}\right)^2 = \frac{4}{9}$$ Square the new number

$$x^2 - \frac{4}{3}x + \frac{4}{9} = \frac{1}{9} + \frac{4}{9}$$ Add the squared number to both sides.

Step 5: **Factor the left side**:

$$\left(x - \frac{2}{3}\right)^2 = \frac{5}{9}$$ Factor.

Step 6: **Use the square root property and rationalize the denominator**:

$$x - \frac{2}{3} = \pm\sqrt{\frac{5}{9}}$$

$$x - \frac{2}{3} = \pm\frac{\sqrt{5}}{3} \qquad \text{then} \qquad x = \frac{2}{3} \pm \frac{\sqrt{5}}{3}$$

Completing the Square to Solve $ax^2 + bx + c = 0$, $a \neq 0$:
1. If $a \neq 1$, multiply both sides by $1/a$. then rewrite the equation so that the constant is alone on one side of the equal sign. 2. Square half the coefficient of x, and add the squared number to both sides. 3. Factor the left side, and use the square root property.

Example 5. Solve $2x^2 - 3x - 1 = 0$ by using the completing the square method.

Solution: Given:

$$2x^2 - 3x - 1 = 0$$

$$x^2 - \frac{3}{2}x - \frac{1}{2} = 0$$ Divide by 2 so that x coefficient is 1

$$x^2 - \frac{3}{2}x = \frac{1}{2} \qquad \text{Add } \frac{1}{2} \text{ to both sides}$$

$$x^2 - \frac{3}{2}x + \frac{9}{16} = \frac{1}{2} + \frac{9}{16} \qquad \text{Complete the square } \frac{1}{2}\left(-\frac{3}{2}\right) = -\frac{3}{4}$$

$$\text{and } \left(-\frac{3}{4}\right)^2 = \frac{9}{16}$$

$$\left(x - \frac{3}{4}\right)^2 = \frac{17}{16} \qquad \text{Factor and simplify}$$

$$x - \frac{3}{4} = \pm\frac{\sqrt{17}}{4} \qquad \text{Square root of both sides}$$

$$x = \frac{3}{4} \pm \frac{\sqrt{17}}{4} \qquad \text{or} \qquad x = \frac{3 \pm \sqrt{17}}{4}$$

Quadratic Formula:

> **The solutions of the quadratic equation** $ax^2 + bx + c = 0$, where $a \neq 0$, are
>
> $$x = \frac{-b \pm \sqrt{b^2 - 4ac}}{2a}$$

The quadratic formula can be derived by completing the square on the equation: $ax^2 + bx + c = 0$, where $a \neq 0$.

Example 6. Solve $x^2 - 4x + 1 = 0$ using the quadratic formula.

Solution: In this problem $a = 1$, $b = -4$, and $c = 1$. Substitute these values into the quadratic formula.

$$x = \frac{-b \pm \sqrt{b^2 - 4ac}}{2a} \qquad \text{Quadratic formula}$$

$$x = \frac{-(-4) \pm \sqrt{(-4)^2 - 4(1)(1)}}{2(1)}$$

$$x = \frac{4 \pm \sqrt{16 - 4}}{2} \quad = \quad \frac{4 \pm 2\sqrt{3}}{2} \quad = \quad \frac{2(2 \pm \sqrt{3})}{2}$$

$$x = 2 \pm \sqrt{3}$$

The solutions are: $2 + \sqrt{3}$ and $2 - \sqrt{3}$

This problem can be solved using a graphing calculator. See Chapter 6, Example 16

Example 7. Solve $3x^2 - x + 2 = 0$ using the quadratic formula.

Solution: From the given coefficients, we see that $a = 3$, $b = -1$, and $c = 2$. Using the quadratic formula:

$$x = \frac{-(-1) \pm \sqrt{(-1)^2 - 4(3)(2)}}{2(3)}$$

$$x = \frac{1 \pm \sqrt{1 - 24}}{6}$$

$$x = \frac{1 \pm \sqrt{-23}}{6}$$

$$x = \frac{1 \pm i\sqrt{23}}{6}$$

The solutions are two complex numbers.

The Discriminant

The quantity under the radical in the quadratic formula, $b^2 - 4ac$, is called the **discriminant.**

The value of the discriminant can be used to determine whether the solutions will be rational, irrational, or complex numbers.

If the discriminant equals zero, there will be only one solution.

Discriminant	Number of solutions	Kind
Positive, perfect square	two	rational
Positive, not perfect square	two	irrational
Zero	one	rational
Negative	two	complex

In Example 6, the equation is $x^2 - 4x + 1 = 0$ and the discriminant is equal to 12 indicating there are two irrational solutions.

In Example 7, the equation is: $3x^2 - x + 2 = 0$ and the discriminant is equal to -23 indicating there are two complex solutions.

Quadratic Type Equations

These are equations in which the highest degree is not 2.
You can identify this type of equation by verifying that the lead term's exponent is the square of the middle term's exponent.

> An equation is of **quadratic type** if it can be written in the form:
>
> $$au^2 + bu + c = 0 \qquad \text{where } a \neq 0 \text{ and } u \text{ is an expression in some variable.}$$

We first find solutions in terms of u and then the solutions of the given equation.

Example 8. Solve $x^6 + 7x^3 = 8$

Solution:

$$x^6 + 7x^3 - 8 = 0 \qquad \text{Make one side zero}$$

Let $u = x^3$, then the equation becomes:

$$u^2 + 7u - 8 = 0$$

$$(u + 8)(u - 1) = 0 \qquad \text{Factor}$$

$$u = -8, u = 1 \qquad \text{Solve for } u$$

Replace u with x^3

$$x^3 = -8 \text{ and } x^3 = 1 \qquad \text{Take the cube root}$$

$$x = -2, \text{ and } x = 1$$

Section 2.3 Exercises

Solve:

1. $x^2 - x - 20 = 0$

2. $x^2 - 6x + 8 = 0$

3. $2x^2 + x - 1 = 0$

4. $3x^2 - x - 2 = 0$

5. $3x^2 - 12x = 0$

6. $5x^2 - 10x = 0$

7. $5x^2 - 20 = 0$

8. $5x^2 = 25$

9. $4x^2 = 26$

10. $2x^2 - 12 = 0$

11. $7x^2 + 14 = 0$

12. $4x^2 + 12 = 0$

13. $5x^2 - 55 = 0$

14. $5x^2 + 55 = 0$

15. $3x^2 - 6 = 0$

16. $3x^2 = 6x$

17. $3x^3 + 5x^2 - 2x = 0$

18. $4x^3 + x^2 - 4x - 1 = 0$

Solve by completing the square:

19. $x^2 + 4x = 5$

20. $x^2 = 7x - 6$

21. $x^2 + 6x + 8 = 0$

22. $x^2 + 7x + 12 = 0$

Solve using the quadratic formula:

23. $x^2 - 7x = 18$

24. $x^2 + x + 3 = 0$

25. $x^2 + 3x - 1 = 0$

26. $8x^2 + 6 = 2x$

Find the discriminant and then determine what type of solutions exist:

27. $3x^2 = 6x + 7$

28. $5x^2 - 10x + 8 = 0$

29. $x^2 - 25 = 0$

Solve:

30. $x^4 - 4x^2 + 3 = 0$

31. $x - 3\sqrt{x} - 4 = 0$

Section 2.4 Graphs of Quadratic Functions

The graph of a quadratic function is called a **parabola.** All expressions of the form
$$y = ax^2 + bx + c$$
where a, b, and c are real numbers with a ≠ 0, have parabolas as graphs.

The graph of $y = x^2$:

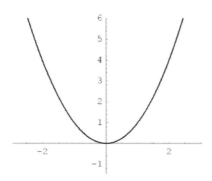

Parabolas are examples of graphs having symmetry about a line (the *y*-axis in the graph above).

The line of symmetry for a parabola is called the **axis** of the parabola.

The point where the axis intersects the parabola is the **vertex** of the parabola.

The vertex will be either the highest point, or maximum, on the graph if the parabola opens down, or it will be the lowest point, or minimum, on the graph if the parabola opens up.

Graphs of Parabolas:

$$y = a(x - h)^2 + k, \quad a \neq 0,$$

1. is a parabola with vertex (*h, k*), and the vertical line *x = h* is the axis;

2. opens upward if *a* > 0 and downward if *a* < 0;

3. is broader than $y = x^2$ if $0 < |a| < 1$ and narrower than $y = x^2$ if $|a| > 1$

Example 1: $y = 5(x-3)^2 - 2$

Solution: This equation is in the form $y = a(x-h)^2 + k$

                   Vertex: $(3, -2)$

                   Axis of symmetry: $x = 3$

                   Maximum   None because $a > 0$ so graph opens up with
no max

                   Minimum -2 because graph opens up and has a min

Example 2: $f(x) = -3(x+4)^2 + 6$

Solution: Vertex: $(-4, 6)$ Axis of symmetry: $x = -4$

             $-3 < 0$ so graph opens down and has a maximum: max is 6

Graph of Quadratic Functions of the type:

$$f(x) = ax^2 + bx + c, \quad a \neq 0$$

The process of completing the square can be used **to change** $ax^2 + bx + c$ to the form $a(x-h)^2 + k$.

Example 3:   Find the vertex, the axis of symmetry, and the maximum or minimum value of : $f(x) = x^2 - 6x + 7$

Solution: To express $f(x) = x^2 - 6x + 7$ in the form $a(x-h)^2 + k$, complete the square on the terms involving x. Take half of the coefficient of x and square it:

$$\left(\frac{-6}{2}\right)^2 = 9$$

Add and subtract that number to the expression:

$$f(x) = x^2 - 6x + 9 - 9 + 7$$
$$= (x^2 - 6x + 9) - 9 + 7$$
$$= (x-3)^2 - 2 \qquad\qquad \text{This is in the form } a(x-h)^2 + k$$

Vertex: $(3, -2)$

Axis of symmetry: $x = 3$

$a > 0$, parabola opens up and has a minimum

Minimum value of function: -2

The graph is:

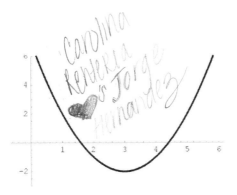

Note that the graph is a shift of $y = x^2$ right 3 units and down 2 units. The axis of symmetry does not show up as part of the graph but is the imaginary line that could be used to fold the graph in half.

This problem can be solved by graphing the given curve using a graphing calculator and then using the CALC function to solve for maximum or minimum.

Example 4: Find the vertex, the axis of symmetry, and the maximum or minimum value of $f(x) = \dfrac{x^2}{2} - 2x + 5$

Solution: Complete the square in order to change the function into the $a(x - h)^2 + k$ form. Begin by factoring ½ out of the first two terms:

$$f(x) = \frac{1}{2}(x^2 - 4x) + 5$$

Next complete the square inside the parentheses. Half of -4 is -2 and $(-2)^2 = 4$. Add and subtract 4 inside the parentheses:

$$f(x) = \frac{1}{2}(x^2 - 4x + 4 - 4) + 5$$

$$= \frac{1}{2}(x^2 - 4x + 4) - \frac{1}{2} * 4 + 5$$

101

$$= \frac{1}{2}(x-2)^2 + 3$$

Vertex: (2, 3)
Axis of Symmetry: $x = 2$
Minimum: 3

Graph:

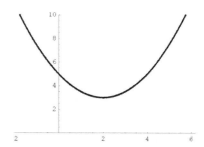

Example 5: Find the vertex, the axis of symmetry and the maximum or minimum value of

$$f(x) = -2x^2 + 8x + 3.$$

Solution: $f(x) = -2x^2 + 8x + 3$.

$= -2(x^2 - 4x) + 3$	Factor -2 out
$= -2(x^2 - 4x + 4 - 4) + 3$	Complete the square
$= -2(x^2 - 4x + 4) - 2*(-4) + 3$	Distribute
$= -2(x-2)^2 + 11$	

Vertex: (2, 11)

Axis of Symmetry: $x = 2$

Maximum value = 11

24, 5, 15, 17

102

Formula Used to Find the Vertex of a Parabola

The formula for the Vertex of a Parabola:

The vertex of the graph of $f(x) = ax^2 + bx + c$ is given by:

$$\left(-\frac{b}{2a}, f\left(-\frac{b}{2a}\right)\right) \quad \text{or} \quad \left(-\frac{b}{2a}, \frac{b^2 - 4ac}{4a}\right)$$

$$\frac{b}{2a}, \quad \frac{-(b^2 - 4ac)}{4a}$$

Note that the x-coordinate is calculated and the y-coordinate is found by substitution.

Example 6: Given the function $f(x) = -x^2 + 8x - 6$. Find a) the vertex, b) maximum or minimum, c) the range, d) intervals where the function is increasing and decreasing.

Solution:

a) Vertex: using the above formula the x-coordinate of the vertex is:

$$-\frac{b}{2a} = -\frac{8}{2(-1)} = 4$$

$$f(4) = -(4)^2 + 8(4) - 6 = 10$$

the vertex is $(4, 10)$

b) Max or Min: since a is negative, the graph opens down and the 2nd coefficient of the vertex which is 10 is the maximum value of the function.

c) The range is $(-\infty, 10]$

d) Since the graph opens down, the function values increase as we approach the vertex from the left and decrease as we move to the right from the vertex.

Increasing: $(-\infty, 4)$ and   Decreasing: $(4, \infty)$.

Applications

Many real-world problems involve finding the maximum or minimum value of a quadratic function.

Example 7: <u>Maximizing Area</u>. A gardener has 80 feet of fence to enclose a rectangular garden. What is the maximum area that the gardener can enclose? What will the dimensions of the garden be?

Solution: First make a drawing of the rectangular garden. Let w represent the width in feet. Then ½ $(80 - 2w)$ or $(40 - w)$ft. represents the length.

The Area of a rectangle is given by length times width:

$$A(w) = (40 - w)w$$

$$= -w^2 + 40w$$

This is a quadratic function and its graph is a parabola.

Since w^2 has a negative coefficient, the function opens down and has a **maximum** value at the vertex.

Find the vertex, which will be $(w, A(w))$

$$w = -\frac{b}{2a} = -\frac{40}{2(-1)} = 20 \text{ ft.}$$

and the length would be:

$$l = 40 - w = 40 - 20 = 20$$

Area would then be: $20 * 20 = 400$ square ft.

Example 8: <u>Height</u>. A model rocket is launched with an initial velocity of 50 ft/sec from the top of a hill that is 30 ft high. Its height t seconds after it has been launched is given by the function:

$$s(t) = -16t^2 + 50t + 30$$

Find the time at which the rocket reaches its maximum height and find this height.

Solution: We will find the maximum value of the given function and the value of time when it occurs.

The function is a quadratic equation and the coefficient of t^2 is negative. We know that the parabola opens downward and has a maximum value at the vertex.

The first coordinate of the vertex gives the time t when the rocket reaches its maximum height.

$$t = -\frac{b}{2a} = -\frac{50}{2(-16)} = 1.562$$

The second coordinate of the vertex gives the maximum height of the rocket.

$$s(1.562) = -16(1.562)^2 + 50(1.562) + 30 = 69.062$$

Section 2.4 Exercises

For the following, find a) the vertex; b) the axis of symmetry; c) determine if there is a maximum or minimum value and find that value.

1. $f(x) = x^2 - 4x - 12$

2. $g(x) = x^2 + 6x - 7$

3. $f(x) = x^2 - 8x + 12$

4. $f(x) = x^2 - 4x + 3$

5. $g(x) = 3x^2 + 9x + 12$

6. $f(x) = -x^2 - 6x + 2$

7. $f(x) = -x^2 - 4x$

8. $g(x) = -x^2 + 4$

9. $f(x) = -3x^2 - 2x + 1$

10. $f(x) = -x^2 - 4x + 2$

11. $f(x) = 2x^2 - 4x + 5$

12. $g(x) = -x^2 + 6x - 6$

Find: a) the vertex; b) determine if there is a maximum or minimum value and find that value; c) the range; d) intervals where the function is increasing and decreasing.

13. $f(x) = x^2 - 7x + 6$

14. $g(x) = x^2 - 4x - 5$

15. $g(x) = -2x^2 + 6x - 5$

16. $f(x) = -2x^2 - 4x + 16$

17.   A ball is thrown directly upward from a height of 4 ft with an initial velocity of 30 ft/sec. The function $s(t) = -16t^2 + 30t + 4$ gives the height of the ball t seconds after it has been thrown. Determine the time at which the ball reaches its maximum height and find the maximum height.

18.   A farmer wants to enclose a rectangular area, using the side of his barn as one side of the rectangle. What is the maximum area that he can enclose with 66 ft of fence? What should the dimensions of the area be in order to give this area?

Section 2.5   Rational, Radical and Absolute Value Equations

> **Rational Equation:** an equation that contains any rational expressions.
>
> The first step in solving a rational equation is to remove fractions:
>   multiply by the Lowest Common Denominator (called LCD) in order to eliminate all of the denominators.

Example 1.   Solve $\dfrac{1}{2} - \dfrac{x-2}{3} = \dfrac{1}{6}$

Solution: The LCD for 2, 3, and 6 is 6. Multiply each side of the equation by 6:

$$\dfrac{1}{2} - \dfrac{x-2}{3} = \dfrac{1}{6} \qquad \text{Given}$$

$$6 * \left(\dfrac{1}{2} - \dfrac{x-2}{3} \right) = 6 * \left(\dfrac{1}{6} \right) \qquad \text{Multiply by LCD of 6}$$

$$6 * \left(\dfrac{1}{2} \right) - 6 * \left(\dfrac{x-2}{3} \right) = 6 * \left(\dfrac{1}{6} \right) \qquad \text{Distribute}$$

$$3 - 2(x-2) = 1 \qquad \text{Simplify}$$

$$3 - 2x + 4 = 1 \qquad \text{Distribute}$$

$$7 - 2x = 1 \qquad \text{Combine like terms}$$

$$-2x = -6 \qquad \text{Subtract 7 from each side}$$

$$x = 3 \qquad \text{Divide both sides by } -2$$

Check: by substitution 3 in the left side of the original equation for x

$$\dfrac{1}{2} - \dfrac{3-2}{3} \quad = \quad \dfrac{1}{2} - \dfrac{1}{3} \quad = \quad \dfrac{3}{6} - \dfrac{2}{6} \quad = \quad \dfrac{1}{6}$$

The solution to the equation is 3.   This problem can be solved using a graphing calculator. See Chapter 6, Example 17.

Example 2: Solve: $\dfrac{1}{x} + \dfrac{1}{6} = \dfrac{1}{4}$

Solution: The LCD for x, 6, and 4 is $12x$. Multiply each side of the equation by $12x$

$$\frac{1}{x} + \frac{1}{6} = \frac{1}{4} \qquad \text{Multiply by LCD of } 12x$$

$$12x\left(\frac{1}{x} + \frac{1}{6}\right) = 12x\left(\frac{1}{4}\right) \qquad \text{Distribute}$$

$$12 + 2x = 3x \qquad \text{Subtract}$$
$$12 = x$$

Check:

$$\frac{1}{12} + \frac{1}{6} \quad = \quad \frac{1}{12} + \frac{2}{12} \quad = \quad \frac{3}{12} \quad = \quad \frac{1}{4}$$

The solution to the equation is 12.

Remember:

1. Use the LCD to remove the fractions in an EQUATION only. This is not appropriate when simplifying a rational expression.

2. Always check rational equations because not all possible solutions found by multiplying by the LCD are legal solutions.

Extraneous Solutions:

A number that appears to be a solution but results in a zero in the denominator is called an extraneous solution.

Example 3. Solve the equation: $\dfrac{1}{x} + \dfrac{1}{x-3} = \dfrac{x-2}{x-3}$

Solution: The LCD for x and $x-3$ is $x(x-3)$

$$\frac{1}{x} + \frac{1}{x-3} = \frac{x-2}{x-3} \qquad \text{Given}$$

$$x(x-3)*\frac{1}{x} + x(x-3)*\frac{1}{x-3} = x(x-3)*\frac{x-2}{x-3} \qquad \text{Multiply by LCD}$$

$$x - 3 + x = x(x-2) \qquad \text{Simplify}$$

$$2x - 3 = x^2 - 2x$$

$$0 = x^2 - 4x + 3$$

$$0 = (x-3)(x-1)$$

$$x - 3 = 0 \qquad \text{or} \qquad x - 1 = 0$$

$$x = 3 \qquad \text{or} \qquad x = 1$$

If $x = 3$, the denominator of $x - 3$ has a value of 0, and thus this value is not a solution.

If $x = 1$, the original equation is satisfied.

The only solution to the equation is 1.

We can use a graphing calculator to check the possible solutions. See Chapter 6, Example 18.

Radical Equations

Radical Equation:

any equation that includes a variable under a radical sign.

109

The Squaring Property is used to solve Radical Equations.

Squaring Property of Equality:

Both sides of an equation may be squared, but all solutions must be verified.

If an equation involves radicals, we often raise both sides to a positive power. The solutions of the new equation always contain the solutions of the given equation. In some cases, however, the new equation has solutions that are **not solutions** to the original equation. These are called extraneous solutions.

Always isolate the radical first.

Example 4: Solve $\sqrt{x^2 - 16} = 3$

Solution: $\sqrt{x^2 - 16} = 3$ Given

$\left(\sqrt{x^2 - 16}\right)^2 = 3^2$ Square both sides

$x^2 - 16 = 9$

$x^2 = 25$

$x = \pm 5$

Check each solution:

$$\sqrt{5^2 - 16} = \sqrt{25 - 16} = \sqrt{9} = 3$$

$$\sqrt{(-5)^2 - 16} = \sqrt{25 - 16} = 3$$

Both 5 and -5 are solutions.

Example 5: Solve $x = \sqrt{2x + 3}$

Solution: $x = \sqrt{2x + 3}$ Given

$$x^2 = \left(\sqrt{2x+3}\right)^2 \qquad \text{Square both sides}$$

$$x^2 = 2x + 3$$

$$x^2 - 2x - 3 = 0$$

$$(x-3)(x+1) = 0$$

$x - 3 = 0$	or	$x + 1 = 0$	
$x = 3$	or	$x = -1$	

Check: $\quad x = 3 \qquad\qquad$ or $\qquad\qquad x = -1$

$$3 = \sqrt{2*3+3} \qquad\qquad\qquad -1 = \sqrt{2(-1)+3}$$

$$3 = \sqrt{9} \qquad\qquad\quad \text{or} \qquad\qquad -1 = \sqrt{1}$$

$$\text{Correct} \qquad\qquad\qquad\qquad \text{Incorrect}$$

Because -1 does not satisfy the original equation, it is an extraneous solution.

The only solution is 3.

Example 6: Solve: $\quad x + 2 = \sqrt{-2-3x}$

Solution: $\qquad\qquad x + 2 = \sqrt{-2-3x} \qquad\qquad \text{Given}$

$$(x+2)^2 = \left(\sqrt{-2-3x}\right)^2 \qquad \text{Square both sides}$$

$$x^2 + 4x + 4 = -2 - 3x$$

$$x^2 + 7x + 6 = 0$$

$$(x+6)(x+1) = 0$$

$x + 6 = 0$	or	$x + 1 = 0$	
$x = -6$	or	$x = -1$	

Check: $\qquad x = -6 \qquad\qquad\qquad\qquad x = -1$

$$-6+2 = \sqrt{-2-3(-6)} \qquad\qquad -1+2 = \sqrt{-2-3(-1)}$$
$$-4 = \sqrt{16} \qquad\qquad\qquad 1 = \sqrt{1}$$
$$\text{Incorrect} \qquad\qquad\qquad \text{Correct}$$

The solution -6 does not check. **The only solution to the original equation is -1.**

Example 7: Solve $\sqrt{x-3} = 5 - \sqrt{x+2}$

Solution:

$\sqrt{x-3} = 5 - \sqrt{x+2}$	Given
$(\sqrt{x-3})^2 = \left(5 - \sqrt{x+2}\right)^2$	Square both sides
$x - 3 = 25 - 10\sqrt{x+2} + x + 2$	
$-30 = -10\sqrt{x+2}$	Combine like terms
$3 = \sqrt{x+2}$	Isolate the radical
$3^2 = (\sqrt{x+2})^2$	Square both sides
$9 = x + 2$	
$x = 7$	

Check:

$\sqrt{x-3} = 5 - \sqrt{x+2}$	Given
$\sqrt{7-3} = 5 - \sqrt{7+2}$	Substitute 7 for x
$\sqrt{4} = 5 - \sqrt{9}$	
$2 = 5 - 3$	
$2 = 2$	

The solution to the given equation is 7.

Absolute Value Equations

To Solve Equations with Absolute Value Terms :

    1. Isolate the absolute value term so that $\left|\, \text{expression} \,\right| = a$

    2. Set the expression within the absolute value
       $= +a$ and $= -a$.

         For $a > 0$, and
              $\left|\, \text{expression} \,\right| = a$ then absolute value symbols are
                      removed by:

             $\text{expression} = a$ or $\text{expression} = -a$

Example 8: Solve: $\left|\, x \,\right| = 8$

Solution: Given $\left|\, x \,\right| = 8$

                    $x = 8$ or $x = -8$

Check: $\left|\, x \,\right| = 8$ $\left|\, x \,\right| = 8$

          $\left|\, 8 \,\right| = 8$ $\left|\, -8 \,\right| = 8$ Both answers are correct.

Example 9: Solve $\left|\, x+1 \,\right| + 4 = 7$

Solution: $\left|\, x+1 \,\right| + 4 = 7$ Isolate the absolute symbol

              $\left|\, x+1 \,\right| = 3$

           $x + 1 = 3$ or $x + 1 = -3$

              $x = 2$ or $x = -4$

113

Check: For $x = 2$

$$|x + 1| + 4 = 7 \qquad \text{Given}$$

$$|2 + 1| + 4 = 7 \qquad \text{Substitute 2 for } x$$

$$3 + 4 = 7$$

$$7 = 7$$

Correct

For $x = -4$

$$|x + 1| + 4 = 7 \qquad \text{Given}$$

$$|-4 + 1| + 4 = 7 \qquad \text{Substitute } -4 \text{ for } x$$

$$|-3| + 4 = 7$$

$$3 + 4 = 7$$

$$7 = 7$$

Correct

The solutions are 2 and -4 since both check.

Absolute value equations can be solved using a graphing calculator. See Chapter 6, Example 19.

Section 2.5 Exercises

Solve:

1. $\dfrac{1}{4} + \dfrac{1}{6} = \dfrac{1}{y}$

2. $\dfrac{3}{x} + \dfrac{1}{2} = \dfrac{3}{4}$

3. $\dfrac{1}{x} + \dfrac{1}{2} = \dfrac{3}{4}$

4. $\dfrac{4}{y} - \dfrac{1}{2} = 3$

5. $\dfrac{1}{t} + \dfrac{1}{5} = \dfrac{t-1}{5t} + \dfrac{3}{10}$

6. $\dfrac{2}{x} + \dfrac{1}{4x} = \dfrac{5}{8}$

7. $\dfrac{x}{2} = \dfrac{5}{x+3}$

8. $\dfrac{x}{3} = \dfrac{6}{x+7}$

9. $\dfrac{x-1}{x^2-4} + \dfrac{1}{x-2} = \dfrac{x+4}{x+2}$

10. $\dfrac{17+y}{y^2-1} - \dfrac{y-2}{y-1} = \dfrac{1}{y+1}$

11. $\dfrac{1}{x-1} + \dfrac{2}{x} = \dfrac{x}{x-1}$

12. $\dfrac{4}{m} + \dfrac{3}{m-3} = \dfrac{m}{m-3} - \dfrac{1}{3}$

13. $\dfrac{5}{x+2} - \dfrac{x-1}{x-3} = -\dfrac{2}{x-3}$

14. $\dfrac{5}{x-3} - 1 = \dfrac{x+7}{2x-6}$

15. $\dfrac{1}{x} = \dfrac{1}{x^3}$

16. $\dfrac{2}{x} = \dfrac{2}{x^2}$

Given:

17. $\sqrt{3x-1} = -5$

18. $\sqrt{3x-4} = -9$

19. $\sqrt{x} = x$

20. $\sqrt{x-2} = x$

21. $y+1 = \sqrt{2y+10}$

22. $\sqrt{2y+18} = y-3$

23. $|x| = 4$

24. $|x| = -4$

25. $|x+3| = 6$

26. $|x+4| = 8$

27. $|x-3| = 7$

28. $|x| = 0$

29. $|x+2| + 4 = 6$

30. $|2x+6| = 4$

115

Section 2.6: Linear Inequalities

Inequality:

An inequality says that one expression is <u>greater than</u>, <u>greater than or equal to</u>, <u>less than</u>, or <u>less than or equal to</u> another.

An inequality uses the following symbols: $<, >, \leq, \geq$

A value of the variable for which the inequality is true is a <u>solution</u> of the inequality.

The <u>solution set</u> is the set of all solutions to the inequality.

<u>Equivalent inequalities</u> are inequalities that have the same solution set.

The techniques used to solve inequalities are very similar to those used to solve equations.

Properties of Inequalities:

If *P, Q,* and *R* are algebraic expressions, then:

$P < Q$ and $P + R < Q + R$ are equivalent.
(The same expression may be added to both sides of an inequality.)

If $R > 0$, then $P < Q$ and $PR < QR$ are equivalent.
(The same <u>positive</u> expression may be multiplied on both sides of an inequality.)

If $R < 0$, then $P < Q$ and $PR > QR$ are equivalent.
(The same <u>negative</u> expression may be multiplied on both sides of an inequality, as long as the direction of the inequality is changed.)

Remember: If both sides of an inequality are multiplied by a negative number, then the <u>direction of the inequality is reversed.</u>

> **Linear Inequalities:** An example of a linear inequality is a first-degree inequality with one variable.

Example 1: Solve: $2x - 4 < 6 - 3x$ and graph the solution.

Solution:

$2x - 4 < 6 - 3x$	Given
$5x - 4 < 6$	Add $3x$ to both sides
$5x < 10$	Add 4 to both sides
$x < 2$	Divide both sides by 5

The solution in interval form is: $(-\infty, 2)$.

Graph:

This problem can be solved using a Graphing Calculator. See Chapter 6, Example 20.

Example 2: Solve $26 - 14x > 20x - 8$ and graph.

Solution:

$26 - 14x > 20x - 8$	Given
$26 - 34x > -8$	Subtract $20x$ from both sides
$-34x > -34$	Subtract 26 from both sides
$x < -1$	Divide both sides by -34 Change direction of inequality

The solution in interval form is : $(-\infty, -1)$.

Graph:

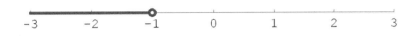

Compound Inequalities:

Compound Inequalities are formed when two inequalities are joined using the word "and" or "or".

Example: $-5 < 2x + 3$ and $2x + 3 \leq 7$

These can be combined into one compound inequality:

$-5 < 2x + 3 \leq 7$

Example 3:   Solve $-5 < 2x + 3 \leq 7$

Solution: Solve this type of inequality by isolating the variable in the middle term.

$-5 < 2x + 3 \leq 7$ Given

$-8 < 2x \leq 4$ Subtract 3 from each part

$-4 < x \leq 2$ Divide by 2

The solution in interval form is: $(-4, 2]$

Graph:

Example 4:   Solve $2x - 5 \leq -3$ or $2x - 5 > 3$

Solution: Solve this type of inequality by solving each part separately.

$2x - 5 \leq -3$ or $2x - 5 > 3$ Given

$2x \leq 2$ or $2x > 8$ Add 5 to both sides in each

$x \leq 1$ or $x > 4$ Divide both sides by 2

The solution in interval form is: $(-\infty, 1] \cup (4, \infty)$

118

Graph:

Inequalities with Absolute Value

Properties of Absolute Value Inequalities:

    1. $|a| < b$ can be written as $-b < a < b$

    2. $|a| > b$ can be written as $a < -b$ **or** $a > b$

Example 5: $|x| < 5$ can be written as $-5 < x < 5$

                   $|x| \geq 3$ can be written as $x \leq -3$ or $x \geq 3$

                   $|3x + 2| < 6$ can be written as $-6 < 3x + 2 < 6$

Example 6:   Solve $|3x + 2| < 6$

Solution: $|3x + 2| < 6$ Given

                         $-6 < 3x + 2 < 6$ Rewrite without absolute symbols

                         $-8 < 3x < 4$ Subtract 2

                         $-8/3 < x < 4/3$ Divide by 3

The solution in interval form is: $(-8/3, 4/3)$

Example 7: Solve $\left| 4x + 4 \right| \geq 8$ and graph.

Solution: $\left| 4x + 4 \right| \geq 8$ Given

$4x + 4 \geq 8$ or $4x + 4 \leq -8$ Remove absolute symbols

$4x \geq 4$ or $4x \leq -12$ Subtract 4

$x \geq 1$ or $x \leq -3$ Divide by 4

The solution in interval form is: $(-\infty, -3\,] \cup [\,1, \infty\,)$. The graph is:

Section 2.6 Exercises

Solve and graph:

1. $x + 5 < 4x - 10$

2. $2x - 6 \leq 3x + 4$

3. $4x - 4 - 2x \geq 2 - 4x + 10$

4. $10 - 4y \leq 3y - 4$

5. $-\dfrac{1}{3}x \leq \dfrac{5}{4} + \dfrac{5}{6}x$

6. $2x(x - 4) < 2(x^2 - 4)$

Solve and write solution in interval form:

7. $-4 \leq x + 1 < 5$

8. $3 \leq x - 4 \leq 5$

9. $-2 \leq x - 3 < 4$

10. $-2 < x + 2 < 4$

11. $-4 \leq -2x < 8$

12. $-3 < \dfrac{1}{2}(3x - 6)$

13. $2x < 10$ or $x + 4 > 16$

14. $2x + 2 < 6$ or $2x + 2 \geq 16$

15. $x + 10 \leq 1/3$ or $x - 20 \geq \frac{1}{2}$

16. $|x| < 4$

17. $|x| < 6$

18. $|x| > 9$

19. $|x + 3| < 6$

20. $|x + 4| < 7$

21. $|x + 7| \geq 9$

22. $|x + 2| > 6$

23. $|x - 1/4| < 6$

24. $|3x| > 6$

25. $|2x + 4| \leq 10$

26. $|4 - 3x| > 8$

27. $|x + 4/3| \leq 8/3$

28. $\left|\dfrac{2x + 1}{5}\right| > 10$

29. $\left|\dfrac{2x - 2}{3}\right| > 8$

30. $|2x + 3| < 5$

Chapter 2 Summary

Tools for Solving Equations:

Addition Property of Equality
If $a = b$, then $a + c = b + c$

Subtraction Property of Equality
If $a = b$, then $a - c = b - c$

Multiplication Property of Equality

If $a = b$, then $ac = bc$ $(c \neq 0)$

Division Property of Equality

If $a = b$, then $a/c = b/c$ $(c \neq 0)$

Square Root Property of Equality
If $a = b$, then $\sqrt{a} = \sqrt{b}$

Power Property of Equality
If $a = b$, then $a^n = b^n$

Zero of a Function:

Given function, f. If a is input into the function as the variable and the result is $f(a) = 0$, then a is a zero of the function.

Complex Number: $a + bi$, a and b real, $i = \sqrt{-1}$, $i^2 = -1$

Imaginary Number: $a + bi$, $b \neq 0$

Complex Conjugates: $a + bi$ and $a - bi$

Quadratic Equations: $ax^2 + bx + c = 0, a \neq 0, a,b,c\ real$

Quadratic Function: $f(x) = ax^2 + bx + c, a \neq 0, a,b,c\ real$

Quadratic Formula: for $ax^2 + bx + c = 0, a \neq 0$

$$x = \frac{-b \pm \sqrt{b^2 - 4ac}}{2a}$$

Tools for Solving Inequalities:

Addition Property of Inequalities
If $P < Q$, then $P + R < Q + R$
If $P \leq Q$, then $P + R \leq Q + R$

Multiplication Property of Inequalities
For $R > 0$
If $P < Q$, then $PR < QR$
If $P \leq Q$, then $PR \leq QR$

For $R < 0$
If $P < Q$, then $PR > QR$
If $P \leq Q$, then $PR \geq QR$

Absolute Value Equations and Inequalities
For $b > 0$

$|a| = b$ can be written as $a = b$ or $a = -b$

$|a| < b$ can be written as $-b < a < b$

$|a| > b$ can be written as $a < -b$ or $a > b$

Chapter 2 Review

Solve:

1. $5x - 4 = 1$

2. $2x - 5 = 5x + 7$

3. $4(x - 2) = 2(x + 3)$

4. $(2x - 1)(3x + 2) = 0$

5. $x^2 + x - 6 = 0$

6. $3x^2 = 8 - 2x$

7. $4x^2 = 20$

8. $x^2 - 6 = 0$

Find the zeros of the function:

9. $f(x) = 6x - 24$

10. $f(x) = x - 5$

11. $f(x) = 3 - 9x$

12. $f(x) = x^2 + 2x + 1$

13. $f(x) = x^2 - 2x - 24$

14. $f(x) = 2x^2 + 5x - 3$

Solve:

15. $\dfrac{4}{x + 2} + \dfrac{2}{x - 1} = 0$

16. $\dfrac{3}{x} + \dfrac{2}{x + 1} = 0$

17. $\sqrt{3x + 2} = \sqrt{5x + 1}$

18. $-1 = \sqrt{x - 4} - \sqrt{x - 1}$

19. $|x - 3| = 4$

20. $|2x + 3| = 15$

Solve, graph and write solution in interval form:

21. $-4 \le 2x + 1 \le 5$

22. $-1 < 2x - 3 \le 7$

23. $3x < -6$ or $x + 2 > 5$

24. $4x + 2 \le 6$ or $2x \ge 10$

25. $|4x - 1| < 3$

26. $|x + 5| \ge 3$

27. Solve $V = lwh$ for h

28. Solve $v = \sqrt{3gp}$ for g

Express in terms of i:

29. $-\sqrt{-20}$

30. $\sqrt{-6} * \sqrt{-12}$

31. $\dfrac{\sqrt{-36}}{-\sqrt{-64}}$

32. $\sqrt{-48} * \sqrt{-12}$

Write in $a + bi$ form.

33. $(4 + 2i)(5 + i)$

34. $(4 - 2i) - 2(-3i)$

35. $\dfrac{2 - 3i}{1 - 2i}$

36. $\dfrac{3 - i}{3 + i}$

Solve using the quadratic formula.

37. $3x^2 - 10x - 8 = 0$

38. $y^2 - 4y + 10 = 0$

39. $x^2 - 3x = 18$

40. $x^4 - 3x + 2 = 0$

CHAPTER 3

POLYNOMIAL AND RATIONAL FUNCTIONS

3.1 Polynomial Functions

3.2 Graphs of Polynomial Functions

3.3 Division of Polynomials

3.4. Zeros of Polynomials

3.5 Rational Functions

3.6 Polynomial and Rational Inequalities

Section 3.1 Polynomial Functions

Polynomial Function:

A polynomial function of degree n is a function of the form:

$$f(x) = a_n x^n + a_{n-1} x^{n-1} + \ldots + a_1 x + a_0$$

for real numbers $a_n, a_{n-1}, \ldots, a_1$ and a_0; with $a_n \neq 0$

Leading Coefficient : the first nonzero coefficient, a_n

Leading Term : the term $a_n x^n$

Degree : is the exponent of the leading term which is n

The coefficients of a polynomial function are real numbers and the exponents are whole numbers.

Examples of Polynomial Functions:

Polynomial Function	Degree	Example
Constant	0	$f(x) = 4$
Linear	1	$f(x) = 2x - 3$
Quadratic	2	$f(x) = 3x^2 + x - 4$
Cubic	3	$f(x) = x^3 + 2x^2 - 3x + 5$
Quartic	4	$f(x) = x^4 + x^2 - x + 2$

The function $f(x) = 0$ has <u>no degree</u> since $f(x) = 0 = 0x = 0x^2 = 0x^7 = 0x^{49}$

QUADRATIC FUNCTION:

Function: $f(x) = x^2 - 2x - 8$
$\qquad\qquad = (x - 4)(x + 2)$

Graph:

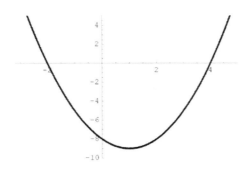

Zeros: $\quad 4, -2$

$\qquad$ x-intercepts: $\quad (4, 0), (-2, 0)$

y-intercept: $\quad (0, -8)$

Minimum: $\quad -9$ at $x = 1$

Maximum: $\quad$ none

Domain: $\qquad (-\infty, +\infty)$ All real numbers

Range: $\qquad [-9, \infty)$

CUBIC FUNCTION:

Function: $f(x) = x^3 + 3x^2 - x - 3$

$$(x+3)(x+1)(x-1)$$

Graph:

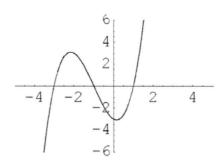

Zeros: $-3, -1, 1$

x-intercepts: $(-3, 0), (-1, 0), (1, 0)$

y-intercept: $(0, -3)$

Relative Minimum: -3.08 at $x = 0.155$

Relative Maximum: 3.08 at $x = -2.15$

Domain: $(-\infty, +\infty)$ All real numbers

Range: $(-\infty, +\infty)$ All real numbers

Notes on Graphs of Polynomials:

Graph is <u>continuous</u> with no breaks, jumps, or holes.

Graph is <u>smooth</u> with no sharp corners.

Domain is $(-\infty, \infty)$ or all real numbers

130

The Leading Term & End Behavior:

The behavior of the graph of a polynomial function as the variable x becomes very large and approaches infinity or very small and approaches minus infinity is called the **end behavior** of the graph. The leading term of a polynomial function defines its end behavior.

Look at the graphs below. Notice that the first 3 graphs are graphs of functions of even degree with the leading coefficient positive.

$$f(x) = 3x^2$$

$$f(x) = 2x^6$$

$$f(x) = 5x^{10}$$

All three of these graphs have the same end behavior.

Now we will change the sign of the leading coefficients.

$f(x) = -3x^2$

$f(x) = -2x^6$

$f(x) = -5x^{10}$

All three of these graphs have the same end behavior.

Now, let's look at two graphs of functions of <u>odd degree.</u>

$f(x) = 3x^3$

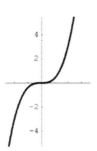

$f(x) = 2x^7$

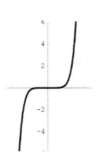

Both of these graphs have the same end behavior.

132

Next, we will **change the sign of the leading coefficients** of these odd degree graphs:

$f(x) = -3x^3$

$f(x) = -2x^7$

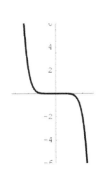

These graphs have the same end behavior

A summary of the end behavior of polynomial functions

Leading-Term Information about the Graphs:

Degree Even:
       Leading Coefficient Positive: the end behavior approaches $+\infty$

       Leading Coefficient Negative: end behavior approaches $-\infty$

Degree Odd:
       Leading Coefficient Positive:
              as x approaches $-\infty$, the end behavior approaches $-\infty$
              as x approaches $+\infty$, the end behavior approaches $+\infty$

       Leading Coefficient Negative:
              as x approaches $-\infty$, the end behavior approaches $+\infty$
              as x approaches $+\infty$, the end behavior approaches $-\infty$

Example 1: Using the leading-term information, match each of the following functions with one of the graphs below:

a. $f(x) = 2x^4 - x^3 + 1$

b. $f(x) = -2x^3 - x^2 + 2x + 1$

c. $f(x) = 3x^5 + x + 2$

d. $f(x) = -4x^6 + x^5 - 2x^3$

1.

2.

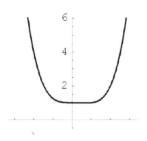

3.

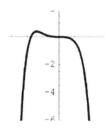

4.

Solution:

	LEADING TERM	DEGREE OF LEAD TERM	SIGN OF LEAD COEF	GRAPH
a)	$2x^4$	Even	Plus	2
b)	$-2x^3$	Odd	Minus	3
c)	$3x^5$	Odd	Plus	4
d)	$-4x^6$	Even	Minus	1

134

Zeros of a Polynomial Function

Given: $f(x) = x^2 - 2x - 3$

To find the zeros, set $f(x) = 0$ and solve:

$$x^2 - 2x - 3 = 0$$
$$(x - 3)(x + 1) = 0$$
$$x - 3 = 0 \qquad x + 1 = 0$$
$$x = 3, -1$$

Solutions of $f(x) = 0$ are the zeros.

Zeros: $3, -1$

The zeros are the x-coordinates *of* x-intercepts of the graph of the function.

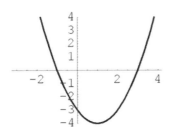

Example 2: Find the zeros of $f(x) = (x + 3)(x + 2)(x - 1)$

Solution: Given: $f(x) = (x + 3)(x + 2)(x - 1)$

$$(x + 3)(x + 2)(x - 1) = 0 \qquad \text{Set } f(x) = 0 \text{ and solve}$$

$$x + 3 = 0 \qquad x + 2 = 0 \qquad x - 1 = 0$$

$$x = -3, -2, 1$$

The zeros of $f(x)$ are $-3, -2, 1$ and

$f(-3) = 0; \ f(-2) = 0; \ f(1) = 0$

If a is a real zero of a function then $f(a) = 0$,

and

a is the x-coordinate of the x-intercept of the graph of the function.

Example 3: If $g(x) = x^3 - 2x^2 - x + 2$. Are 2 and 3 zeros of $g(x)$?

Solution: Given $g(x) = x^3 - 2x^2 - x + 2$

To decide if each number, c, is a zero, we will find the values of $g(c)$

$$g(2) = 2^3 - 2(2)^2 - 2 + 2 = 8 - 8 - 2 + 2 = 0$$

Since $g(2) = 0$, 2 is a zero of $g(x)$.

$$g(3) = 3^3 - 2(3)^2 - 3 + 2 = 27 - 18 - 3 + 2 = 8$$

Since $g(3) \neq 0$, 3 is not a zero of $g(x)$.

Graph :

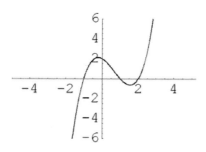

Example 4: Find the zeros of
$$f(x) = 3(x + 2)(x - 2)(x - 2)(x - 2)$$
$$= 3(x + 2)(x - 2)^3$$

Solution: To find the zeros, set $f(x) = 0$ and solve

$$x + 2 = 0 \qquad x - 2 = 0$$
$$x = -2, 2$$

The zeros of $f(x)$ are -2 and 2.

Example 5: Find the zeros of
$$g(x) = -(x-3)(x-3)(x+4)(x+4)$$

$$= -(x-3)^2(x+4)^2$$

Solution: To find the zeros, we will set $g(x) = 0$ and solve

$$x+4 = 0 \qquad x-3 = 0$$

$$x = -4, 3$$

The zeros of $f(x)$ are -4 and 3.

Looking back at Example 4 and Example 5, we see that several factors occur more than once.

In Example 4 the factor $(x-2)$ occurs three times. The zero found from this factor, 2, has a **multiplicity of 3**. The factor $(x+2)$ occurs once. The zero found from this factor, -2, has a **multiplicity of 1**.

In Example 5 the factor $(x-3)$ occurs twice. The zero found from this factor, 3, has a **multiplicity of 2**. The factor $(x+4)$ occurs twice. The zero found from this factor, -4, has a **multiplicity of 2**.

Multiplicity Relationship to Graphs:

Multiplicity of a zero is either odd or even

If $(x-a)^k$ where $k \geq 1$, is a factor of a polynomial function and $(x-a)^{k+1}$ does not exist:

if k is <u>odd</u>, then the graph crosses the axis at $(a, 0)$

if k is <u>even</u>, then the graph is tangent to the axis at $(a, 0)$

Example 6:   Find the zeros of: $f(x) = x^3 - 2x^2 - 4x + 8$ and describe the graph at these zeros

Solution: $f(x) = x^3 - 2x^2 - 4x + 8$ Given

$\qquad\qquad f(x) = x^2(x-2) - 4(x-2)$ Factor by grouping

$\qquad\qquad\qquad = (x-2)(x^2 - 4)$

$\qquad\qquad\qquad = (x-2)(x-2)(x+2)$

$\qquad\qquad\qquad = (x-2)^2(x+2)$

The zeros are:

$\qquad\qquad$ 2 with a multiplicity of 2, and -2 of a multiplicity of 1.

At the x-intercept $(2, 0)$ the graph is tangent to the axis.

At the x-intercept $(-2, 0)$ the graph crosses the axis.

Graph: $f(x) = x^3 - 2x^2 - 4x + 8$

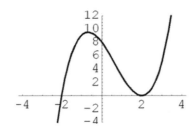

This problem can be solved using a graphing calculator. See Chapter 6, Example 21

Example 7:   Find the zeros of : $f(x) = x^4 + 3x^2 - 54$ and describe the graph at these zeros

Solution: Given $f(x) = x^4 + 3x^2 - 54$

$$f(x) = (x^2 + 9)(x^2 - 6) \qquad\qquad \text{Factor}$$

$$x^2 + 9 = 0 \quad \text{and} \quad x^2 - 6 = 0 \qquad\qquad \text{Solve each factor}$$

$$x^2 = -9 \qquad\qquad\qquad x^2 = 6$$

$$x = \pm\sqrt{-9} = \pm 3i \qquad\qquad x = \pm\sqrt{6}$$

The zeros are $\pm\, 3i$ and $\pm\sqrt{6}$

Look at the graph of the function in Example 7:

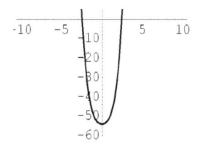

Only the real-number zeros of a function correspond to the x-intercepts of the graph. The real-number zeros of $\pm\sqrt{6}$ are seen on the graph of the function, but the zeros $\pm\, 3i$ are not real-numbers and are not seen on the graph.

Finding Real Zeros Using a Graphing Calculator:

With many functions it is very difficult to find the exact values of the zeros. A graphing calculator will give an approximate value of the real-number zeros.

See Chapter 6, Example 22 for an example of such a function.

Section 3.1 Exercises:

Tell whether the given polynomial is constant, linear, quadratic, cubic, or quartic and find the leading term, the leading coefficient, and the degree of the polynomial.

1. $f(x) = 3x^4 - 7x + 5$

2. $g(x) = 12x^3 - 4$

3. $f(x) = 0.3x - 2.3$

4. $h(x) = -3$

5. $g(x) = 134x^2 + x - 2$

6. $f(x) = -6x^2 - 2x$

7. $h(x) = -3x^3 - x^2 + 5x$

8. $f(x) = 4 - x$

9. $f(x) = -5$

10. $f(x) = 17x - x^2$

Describe the end behavior of the graph of each function:

11. $f(x) = -5x^3 - 2x + 4$

12. $g(x) = 0.5x^4 + 0.3x^3 - .0.7x$

13. $h(x) = -2x^6 + 8x^4$

14. $f(x) = 2x^5 - 3x^6$

15. $g(x) = 10 + 2x^5 + x$

16. $h(x) = 2x - 3x^4 + 2x^5$

Find the zeros of the polynomial function and state the multiplicity of each:

17. $f(x) = (x - 3)^2(x - 4)$

18. $g(x) = (x^2 - 4)^3$

19. $h(x) = -3(x - 2)(x - 2)(x - 2)(x + 2)$

20. $f(x) = x^3(x - 5)^2(x + 1)$

21. $f(x) = -2(x - 1)^2(x + 5)^3 x^4$

22. $g(x) = x^4 - 17x^2 + 16$

3.2   Graphs of Polynomial Functions

> If a polynomial function $f(x)$ of degree n is graphed, the graph will have:
>
> at most n real x-intercepts and thus at most $\underline{n \ \text{zeros}}$
>
> at most $n-1$ turning points called relative maxima and minima
>
> maxima/minima occur when the graph of the function changes from decreasing to increasing or from increasing to decreasing.

Example 1:   Graph the polynomial function $f(x) = -3x^4 + 6x^3$

Solution:

Step 1: Use the leading term to find the end behavior of the graph:

The leading term is $-3x^4$.

The degree is 4, even, and the coefficient is negative.

The end behavior is:

As $x \to \infty$, the graph $\to -\infty$

As $x \to -\infty$, the graph $\to -\infty$

The graph will look **somewhat like**:

Step 2: Find the zeros by setting $f(x) = 0$.

$-3x^4 + 6x^3 = 0$

$-3x^3(x - 2) = 0$ Factor to solve

$$-3x^3 = 0 \qquad\qquad x - 2 = 0$$

$$x = 0 \qquad \text{or} \qquad x = 2$$

The zeros are: 0 with multiplicity of 3, and 2 with multiplicity 1

Step 3: Find the intercepts:

The zeros are the x-coordinates of the x-intercepts, so the

x-intercepts are: $(0, 0)$ and $(2, 0)$.

To find the y-intercept, let $x = 0$ in the function:

$$f(x) = -3x^4 + 6x^3$$

$$-3(0)^4 + 6(0)^3 = 0$$

y-intercept is: $(0, 0)$

Step 4: Use the zeros to divide the x-axis into intervals and find whether the graph is above or below the x-axis in each interval.

The zeros are 0 and 2, so the intervals will be

$$(-\infty, 0) \qquad (0, 2) \qquad (2, \infty)$$

Test the sign of the function within each interval.

Interval	Test value	Function value	Sign	Location
$(-\infty, 0)$	-2	-96	$-$	Below x-axis
$(0, 2)$	1	3	$+$	Above x-axis
$(2, \infty)$	3	-81	$-$	Below x-axis

These test points also give point on the graph:

$$(-2, -96); \quad (1, 3); \quad (3, -81)$$

142

Step 5: Add a few more points:

x	$f(x)$	point
-1	-9	$(-1, -9)$
1	3	$(1, 3)$
1.5	5.06	$(1.5, 5.06)$

Step 6: Check the multiplicity of the zeros:

0: multiplicity is 3 (odd), so the graph crosses the axis at this point

2: multiplicity is 1 (odd), so the graph crosses the axis at the point.

Step 7: Draw the graph:

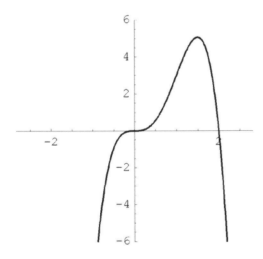

Guide for Graphing a Polynomial Function:

1. Find the end behavior of the graph using the leading term.

2. Find the zeros of the function setting $f(x) = 0$.

3. Find the x-intercepts using the zeros as the first coordinate.
   Find the y-intercept by finding $f(0)$.

4. Divide the x-axis into intervals using the zeros and then use test
   points to find the signs of the function in each interval.

5. Find additional points if needed.

6. Use the multiplicity of each zero to see if the graph crosses the x-axis or
   is tangent to it at the zero.

7. Draw the graph.

Example 2. Graph the polynomial function: $f(x) = x^3 + x^2 - 4x - 4$

Solution:

1. The leading term is x^3, the degree is 3 which is odd, and the coefficient is
   positive. The end behavior is:
   $$\text{as } x \to -\infty, \; f(x) \to -\infty \qquad \text{and} \quad \text{as } x \to \infty, \; f(x) \to \infty$$

   The graph will look **somewhat like**:

   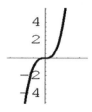

2. Find the zeros by solving $f(x) = 0$.

   $$x^3 + x^2 - 4x - 4 = 0$$

144

$$x^2(x+1) - 4(x+1) = 0 \qquad \text{Factor}$$

$$(x^2 - 4)(x+1) = 0$$

$$(x-2)(x+2)(x+1) = 0$$

The zeros are -2, -1, and 2.

3. The intercepts:

       x-intercepts: (using the zeros) are $(-2,, 0), (-1, 0),$ and $(2, 0)$.

       y-intercept: (finding $f(0)$) is $(0, -4)$

4. Divide into intervals:

Interval	Test value	Function value	Sign	Location
$(-\infty, -2)$	-3	-10	$-$	below axis
$(-2, -1)$	$-3/2$	0.88	$+$	above axis
$(-1, 2)$	1	-6	$-$	below axis
$(2, \infty)$	3	20	$+$	above axis

5. Add points:

x	$f(x)$	point
$-1/2$	-0.88	$(-1/2, -0.88)$
$1/2$	-5.63	$(1/2, -5.63)$
3	20	$(3, 20)$

6: Multiplicity:
All zeros have a multiplicity of 1 and the graph will cross the axis at each.

7. Draw the graph:

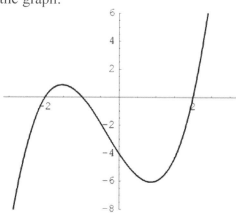

Example 3: Graph the polynomial function $g(x) = (x+1)(x-1)^2(x-3)$

Solution:

1. The leading term is x^4, the degree is 4 which is even, and the coefficient is positive. The end behavior is:

   as $x \to -\infty, f(x) \to \infty$ and   as $x \to \infty, f(x) \to \infty$

   The graph will look somewhat like:

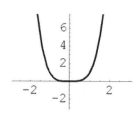

2. Find the zeros by solving $f(x) = 0$.

   $$(x+1)(x-1)^2(x-3) = 0$$

   the zeros are -1, 1, and 3

3. The intercepts:

   x-intercepts, using the zeros are $(-1, 0)$, $(1, 0)$, and $(3, 0)$.

   y-intercept, finding $f(0)$ is $(0, -3)$

146

4. Divide into intervals:

Interval	Test value	Function value	Sign	Location
$(-\infty,-1)$	-2	45	$+$	above axis
$(-1, 1)$	0	-3	$-$	below axis
$(1, 3)$	2	-3	$-$	below axis
$(3,\infty)$	4	45	$+$	above axis

4. Multiplicity:
   zeros of -1 and 3 have multiplicity of 1 (odd) and the graph crosses x-axis

   zero of 1 is multiplicity of 2 (even) and the graph is tangent to the x-axis

5. Draw graph:

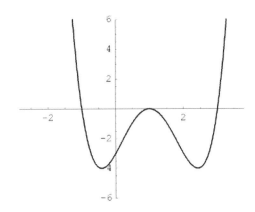

The Intermediate Value Theorem

Much of the work in locating real zeros uses the following theorem, which is related to the fact that graphs of polynomial functions are unbroken curves, with no gaps or sudden jumps.

The Intermediate Value Theorem:

If $P(x)$ is a polynomial function with only real coefficients, and if for real numbers a and b, $P(a)$ and $P(b)$ are opposite in sign, then there exists at least one real zero between a and b.

Example 4: Use the intermediate value theorem to determine whether the given function has a real zero between the given numbers:

$$f(x) = x^3 + 2x^2 - 8x \qquad \text{between} -1 \text{ and } 1, \text{ and between } 1 \text{ and } 3$$

Solution: Find $f(-1)$, $f(1)$, and $f(3)$ and check for different signs.

$$f(-1) = (-1)^3 + 2(-1)^2 - 8(-1) = 9$$

$$f(1) = (1)^3 + 2(1)^2 - 8(1) = -5$$

$$f(3) = (3)^3 + 2(3)^2 - 8(3) = 21$$

Because the signs differ for each set of numbers, the intermediate value theorem says that there exists at least one real zero between -1 and 1 and between 1 and 3.

Look at the graph:

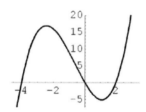

Example 5: . Use the intermediate value theorem to determine whether the given function has a real zero between the given numbers:

$$f(x) = x^4 - 5x^3 \qquad \text{between } 2 \text{ and } 3$$

Solution: Find $f(2)$ and $f(3)$ and see if they have different signs

$$f(2) = (2)^4 - 5(2)^3 = -24 \qquad\qquad f(3) = (3)^4 - 5(3)^3 = -54$$

Both are negative, but this does not necessarily mean that there is no zero between them.

Section 3.2 Exercises:

For each function find:

      a. the maximum number of real zeros that the function can have
      b. the maximum number of x-intercepts that the graph can have
      c. the maximum number of turning points that the graph can have

1. $f(x) = x^6 - 2x^2 + 8$ 2. $f(x) = -x^4 + x^2 - x^6 + 5$

3. $f(x) = 1/2x^3 + 4x^2$ 4. $f(x) = x^8 - 2x^6 + 4x - 8$

5. $f(x) = -2x - x^5$ 6. $f(x) = -5x^4 + 4x^3 - 2x - 6$

For each function find:

      a. the end behavior of the graph
      b. the y-intercept

7. $f(x) = 3/4x^2 - 6$ 8. $f(x) = -2x^4 - 3x^3 - 6x^2 - 2$

9. $f(x) = x^3 - 3x^2 + x - 2$ 10. $f(x) = -2x^5 - x^4 + x^2 + 3$

11. $f(x) = x^9 - x^8 + x + 4$ 12. $f(x) = 5$

Graph each of the polynomial functions using the Guide for graphing polynomials:

13. $f(x) = -2x^3 - 4x^2$ 14. $f(x) = x^5 - 6x^3$

15. $f(x) = -x(x-2)^2(x+1)(x+2)$ 16. $f(x) = x(x-1)(x+1)(x+2)$

Using the intermediate value theorem, determine, if possible, if there is a real zero between the two given numbers:

17. $f(x) = x^3 + 5x^2 - 6x - 11$; for -2, and 1

18. $f(x) = x^3 + 6x^2 - 8x - 10$; for 1, and 2

19. $f(x) = 3x^2 - x - 7$; for -3, and 0

20. $f(x) = -2x^2 - 4x + 6$; for -4, and -2

Section 3.3   Division of Polynomials

If we want to determine if some number, k, is a factor of a larger number, we divide the larger number by k. If the result has no remainder (remainder is zero), then we know that the number k is indeed a factor of the larger number.   We use a similar method to find the factors of a polynomial, and then we can find the zeros of that polynomial.

Dividing Polynomials:
We will begin by using long division of polynomials.

Division:

For any polynomial $P(x)$ and any number k, there exists a unique polynomial $Q(x)$ and number r such that:

$$P(x) \; = \; (x - k) \; * \; Q(x) \; + \; r$$

Example 1.   Use division to determine if $(x + 2)$ and $(x - 2)$ are factors of:

$$x^3 - 3x + 2$$

Solution: Notice that there is no 2nd degree term. Before dividing, add a term of $0x^2$ to the polynomial.

$$x^3 + 0x^2 - 3x + 2$$

Divide by the factor $(x + 2)$:

$$
\begin{array}{r}
x^2 - 2x + 1 \\
x + 2 \overline{\smash{\big)}\ x^3 + 0x^2 - 3x + 2} \\
\underline{x^3 + 2x^2} \\
-2x^2 - 3x \\
\underline{-2x^2 - 4x} \\
x + 2 \\
\underline{x + 2} \\
0
\end{array}
$$

Quotient is $x^2 - 2x + 1$

Remainder is 0

Because the remainder is zero, we know that $(x + 2)$ is a factor.

151

Divide by the factor $(x - 2)$

$$
\begin{array}{r}
x^2 + 2x + 1 \\
x - 2 \overline{)x^3 + 0x^2 - 3x + 2} \\
\underline{x^3 - 2x^2} \\
2x^2 - 3x \\
\underline{2x^2 - 4x} \\
x + 2 \\
\underline{x - 2} \\
4
\end{array}
$$

Quotient is $x^2 + 2x + 1$

Remainder is 4

We find a remainder of 4 rather than zero, so $(x - 2)$ is not a factor.

The Remainder Theorem:

If a polynomial $P(x)$ is divided by $x - k$, then the remainder is $P(k)$.

Use the remainder theorem with the polynomial function given in Example 1:

$$f(x) = x^3 - 3x + 2$$

$$f(-2) = (-2)^3 - 3(-2) + 2 = -8 + 6 + 2 = 0$$

$$f(2) = (2)^3 - 3(2) + 2 = 8 - 6 + 2 = 4$$

These values are the same as the remainders we found in Example 1.

Synthetic Division:

Because we will often use the remainder theorem to find factors of a polynomial, we can use an abbreviated technique to divide polynomials.

Example 2: Look at the two examples below. We will divide using long division and then we will use an abbreviated version with only the number coefficients

$$(5x^3 - 6x^2 - 28x - 2) \div (x + 2)$$

$$
\begin{array}{r}
5x^2 - 16x + 4 \\
x+2\overline{)5x^3 - 6x^2 - 28x - 2} \\
\underline{5x^3 + 10x^2} \\
-16x^2 - 28x \\
\underline{-16x^2 - 32x} \\
4x - 2 \\
\underline{4x + 8} \\
-10
\end{array}
\qquad
\begin{array}{r}
5 - 16 + 4 \\
1+2\overline{)5 - 6 - 28 - 2} \\
\underline{5 + 10} \\
-16 - 28 \\
\underline{-16 - 32} \\
4 \quad -2 \\
\underline{4 \; + \; 8} \\
-10
\end{array}
$$

Notice that the numbers in these two examples are quite similar.

We will abbreviate the second division even further as an example of **synthetic division**.

Synthetic Division: Use the same example.

Since the divisor is $x + 2$, we set the divisor equal to zero and solve and get -2.

    Begin by writing:

$$-2\overline{)\;5 \quad -6 \quad -28 \quad -2\;}$$

    Next, bring down the 5

$$
\begin{array}{r}
-2\overline{)\;5 \quad -6 \quad -28 \quad -2\;} \\
\underline{\hspace{3cm}} \\
5 \hspace{4cm}
\end{array}
$$

Now, multiply -2 by 5 to get -10, and add it to the -6 in the first row

$$
\begin{array}{r|rrrr}
-2 & 5 & -6 & -28 & -2 \\
& & -10 & & \\
\hline
& 5 & -16 & &
\end{array}
\qquad \text{add}
$$

Next, $(-2)(-16) = 32$. Add this to the -28 in the first row.

$$
\begin{array}{r|rrrr}
-2 & 5 & -6 & -28 & -2 \\
& & -10 & 32 & \\
\hline
& 5 & -16 & 4 &
\end{array}
\qquad \text{add}
$$

Finally, $(-2)(4) = -8$, and we add this to -2 and get

$$
\begin{array}{r|rrrr}
-2 & 5 & -6 & -28 & -2 \\
& & -10 & 32 & -8 \\
\hline
& 5 & -16 & 4 & -10
\end{array}
\qquad \text{add}
$$

The coefficients of the quotient polynomial and the remainder are read directly from the bottom row. The degree will be one less than the original polynomial.

The result of the division in the example of synthetic division is written as:

$$5x^3 - 6x^2 - 28x - 2 = (x+2)(5x^2 - 16x + 4) + (-10)$$
$$P(x) \qquad = (x-k) * Q(x) \qquad + \quad r$$

Example 3   Given that $f(x) = 3x^4 - 5x^3 - 2x^2 + x - 4$, find $f(6)$.

Solution: From the remainder theorem, $f(6)$ is equal to the remainder when $f(x)$ is divided by $x - 6$. Use synthetic division to find the remainder:

$$
\begin{array}{c|ccccc}
6 & 3 & -5 & -2 & 1 & -4 \\
& & 18 & 78 & 456 & 2742 \\
\hline
& 3 & 13 & 76 & 457 & 2738
\end{array}
$$

The quotient is $3x^3 + 13x^2 + 76x + 457$ with a remainder of 2738

From the remainder theorem $f(6) = 2738$

Check: $f(x) = 3x^4 - 5x^3 - 2x^2 + x - 4$

$f(6) = 3(6)^4 - 5(6)^3 - 2(6)^2 + (6) - 4 = 2738$

In Example 3 with $f(x) = 3x^4 - 5x^3 - 2x^2 + x - 4$, $f(6)$ can be found using a graphing calculator. See Chapter 6, Example 23.

Example 4: If $f(x) = x^3 + 4x^2 - 9x - 36$, is 3 a zero of $f(x)$?

Solution: We can use synthetic division with the remainder theorem to find $f(3)$.

$$
\begin{array}{c|cccc}
3 & 1 & 4 & -9 & -36 \\
& & 3 & 21 & 36 \\
\hline
& 1 & 7 & 12 & 0
\end{array}
$$

The remainder is 0. Then the remainder theorem shows that $f(3) = 0$. The number 3 is a zero of the function.

The Factor Theorem:

The polynomial $(x - k)$ is a factor of the polynomial $P(x)$ if and only if

$$P(k) = 0$$

Example 5: Given $f(x) = 6x^3 + 19x^2 + 2x - 3$. Find the factors of $f(x)$ and then solve the equation $f(x) = 0$.

155

Solution: Use the remainder theorem to look for factors. Try $(x - 1)$. Use synthetic division to test if $f(1) = 0$

$$
\begin{array}{r|rrrr}
\underline{1} & 6 & 19 & 2 & -3 \\
 &   & 6 & 25 & 27 \\
\hline
 & 6 & 25 & 27 & 24
\end{array}
$$
remainder is 24

Since $f(1) \neq 0,\ x - 1$ is not a factor.

Try $x + 3$

$$
\begin{array}{r|rrrr}
-3 & 6 & 19 & 2 & -3 \\
 &   & -18 & -3 & 3 \\
\hline
 & 6 & 1 & -1 & 0
\end{array}
$$
remainder is 0

Since $f(-3) = 0$, we know that $(x+3)$ is a factor.

$f(x) = 6x^3 + 19x^2 + 2x - 3$ given

$f(x) = (x + 3)(6x^2 + x - 1)$ use the last line from synthetic division

$f(x) = (x+3)(3x - 1)(2x+1)$ now factor the degree 2 factor

Set $f(x) = 0$

$(x+3)(3x - 1)(2x+1) = 0$

$x + 3 = 0 \qquad 3x - 1 = 0 \qquad 2x+1 = 0$

$x = -3,\ 1/3,\ -1/2$

Example 5 can be solved using a graphing calculator. See Chapter 6, Example 24.

Example 6:   Look at the function

$$f(x) = x^3 - 7x - 6$$

Graph:

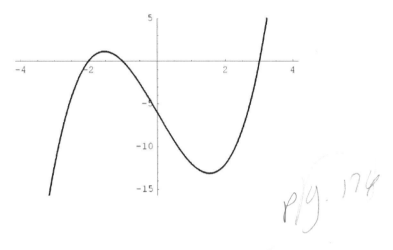

We see that the zeros are $-2, -1,$ and 3.

Solutions/ Zeros/ Remainders of Zero/ *x*-Intercepts/ Factors

Look at the statements below regarding Example 6:

   -2 is a solution of $f(x) = 0$

   -2 is a zero of $f(x)$

   $f(-2) = 0$

   $(-2, 0)$ is an *x*-intercept of the graph

   0 is the remainder when $f(x)$ is divided by $x + 2$

   $(x + 2)$ is a factor of f

Each of these statements mean the same thing and are just stated differently.

The numbers -1 and 3 could also be used in place of -2 in the statements above.

157

Section 3.3 Exercises

Use long division to decide whether or not the second polynomial is a factor of the first.

1. $4x^2 + 2x + 42, \quad x - 3$ 2. $-3x^2 - 4x + 2, \quad x + 2$

3. $x^3 + 2x^2 - 3, \quad x - 1$ 4. $2x^3 + x + 2, \quad x + 2$

5. $4x^3 + 6x^2 - 5x - 2, \quad x + 2$ 6. $2x^4 + 5x^3 - 2x^2 + 5x + 3, \quad x + 3$

In the following, a polynomial $P(x)$ and a divisor $d(x)$ are given. Use long division to find the quotient $Q(x)$ and the remainder $R(x)$ when $P(x)$ is divided by $d(x)$.

7. $P(x) = x^3 - 27, \quad d(x) = x + 2$

8. $P(x) = x^3 + x^2 + x - 8, \quad d(x) = x - 1$

9. $P(x) = 2x^3 - 3x^2 - 5x + 4, \quad d(x) = x - 2$

10. $P(x) = 3x^2 + 8x + 5, \quad d(x) = x + 3$

Use synthetic division to decide whether or not the given number is a zero of the given polynomial.

11. 12, $\quad P(x) = x^2 + 2x - 120$ 12 2, $\quad P(x) = x^3 - 3x^2 + 4x - 4$

13. 4, $\quad P(x) = 2x^3 - 6x^2 - 9x + 4$ 14. -3, $\quad P(x) = x^3 + 2x^2 - x + 6$

Use synthetic division to find the quotient and the remainder.

15. $(x^3 - 64) \div (x - 4)$ 16. $(2x^4 + x^3 - 15x^2 + 3x) \div (x + 3)$

17. $(x^3 + 2x^2 + x - 5) \div (x - 2)$ 18. $(x^3 + x^2 - x - 1) \div (x + 1)$

Use synthetic division to find the function value.

19. $f(x) = 2x^4 + x^3 - 10x^2 - 2, \quad f(-2)$ 20. $f(x) = x^3 - 3x^2 + 4x + 2, \quad f(4)$

Factor the polynomial and solve the equation $f(x) = 0$

21. $f(x) = x^3 + x^2 - 4x - 4$ 22. $f(x) = x^3 + 2x^2 - 9x - 18$

Section 3.4   Zeros of a Polynomial

As a result of the remainder theorem, if $P(k) = 0$, then the remainder when $P(x)$ is divided by $x - k$ is equal to zero.

This means that $x - k$ is a factor of $P(x)$.

Conversely, if $x - k$ is a factor of $P(x)$, then $P(k)$ must equal 0.

Factor Theorem:

> The polynomial $(x - k)$ is a factor of the polynomial $P(x)$ if and only if $P(k) = 0$.

Example 1. Is $(x - 1)$ a factor of $f(x) = 2x^4 + 3x^2 - 5x + 6$?

Solution: By the factor theorem, $(x - 1)$ is a factor of $f(x)$ only if $f(1) = 0$.

Use synthetic division and the remainder theorem to decide.

$$
\begin{array}{r|rrrrr}
\underline{1} & 2 & 0 & 3 & -5 & 6 \\
 &   & 2 & 2 & 5 & 0 \\
\hline
 & 2 & 2 & 5 & 0 & 6
\end{array}
\qquad \text{remainder is 6}
$$

Since the remainder is 6, $f(1) = 6$, not 0, so $(x - 1)$ is **not** a factor of $f(x)$.

Example 2. Is $(x - i)$ a factor of $f(x) = 3x^3 + (-4 - 3i)x^2 + (5 + 4i)x - 5i$

Solution: The only way $(x - i)$ can be a factor of $f(x)$ is if $f(i) = 0$.

Use synthetic division and the remainder theorem to decide.

$$\begin{array}{r|rrrr}
i & 3 & -4-3i & 5+4i & -5i \\
 & & 3i & -4i & 5i \\
\hline
 & 3 & -4 & 5 & 0
\end{array} \quad \text{remainder is } 0$$

Since the remainder is 0, $f(i)$ does $= 0$, and so $(x - i)$ is a factor.

The quotient of $3x^2 - 4x + 5$ found in the synthetic division process is the other factor:

$$f(x) = (x - i)(3x^2 - 4x + 5)$$

Fundamental Theorem of Algebra:

Every polynomial of degree 1 or more has at least one complex zero.

$$P(x) = (x - k) * Q(x)$$

The fundamental theorem and the factor theorem can be used to factor $Q(x)$ in the same way. If $P(x)$ has degree n and repeating the process n times gives:

$$P(x) = a(x - k_1)(x - k_2) \ldots (x - k_n)$$

where a is the leading coefficient of $P(x)$. Each of these factors leads to a zero of $P(x)$, so $P(x)$ has n zeros $k_1, k_2, k_3, \ldots, k_n$.

A polynomial of degree n has at most n distinct zeros.

Finding Polynomials with Known Zeros

If we are given several numbers, we can find a polynomial function with those numbers as zeros.

Example 3: Find a polynomial function of degree 3, having the zeros of 1, $2i$, and $-2i$.

Solution: This polynomial function has factors of $(x-1)$, $(x-2i)$, and $(x+2i)$.

$$f(x) = a_n(x-1)(x-2i)(x+2i) \qquad \text{let } a_n = 1 \text{ for the simplest function}$$

$$= (x-1)(x^2+4) \qquad \text{Multiply } (x-2i)(x+2i)$$

$$= x^3 - x^2 + 4x - 4 \qquad \text{Multiply}$$

Example 4: Find a polynomial of degree 4 with -1 as a zero of multiplicity 3, and 0 as a zero of multiplicity 1.

Solution: Again we will let $a_n = 1$ to get the simplest function.

$$f(x) = (x+1)^3(x-0)$$

$$= x^4 + 3x^3 + 3x^2 + x$$

Conjugate Zeros Theorem

If $P(x)$ is a polynomial having <u>only real coefficients</u> and if
   $a + bi$ is a zero of $P(x)$,
then the conjugate
   $a - bi$ is also a zero of $P(x)$.

This is not true if the coefficients are not real coefficients.

If $P(x)$ is a polynomial having <u>only rational coefficients</u> and if
   $a + b\sqrt{c}$ is a zero of $P(x)$,
then the conjugate
   $a - b\sqrt{c}$ is also a zero of $P(x)$.

Example 5:   If a polynomial function of lowest possible degree with rational coefficients has $-2+4i$, $-3i$,   and $1-\sqrt{2}$ as three of its zeros. Find the other zeros.

Solution: Since the coefficients are rational (and thus real as well), the function must also have zeros of:

$$-2-4i\,, \quad 3i\,, \quad \text{and } 1+\sqrt{2}$$

Example 6:   Find a polynomial of lowest possible degree having real coefficients and zeros of 2 and $2-i$.

Solution: The complex number $2+i$ also must be a zero, so the polynomial has at least 3 zeros, 2, $2-i$, and $2+i$. Since we want the lowest degree, these will be the only zeros.

The three factors must be:

$$(x-2)(x-(2-i))(x-(2+i)) \qquad \text{or} \quad (x-2)(x-2+i)(x-2-i)$$

and

$$f(x) = (x-2)(x-(2-i))(x-(2+i))$$

$$f(x) = (x-2)(x-2+i)(x-2-i)$$

$$f(x) = x^3 - 6x^2 + 13x - 10$$

Rational Zeros of Polynomial Functions

Often it is difficult to find the zeros of a polynomial function. The following theorem gives a useful method for finding a set of possible zeros of a polynomial with integer coefficients.

3.2

1. 6, 6, 5 –
9. $-\infty, \infty$ –
15.
17. yer

3.3

5. yer
9. $2x^2 + x - 3, \ -2$
13. yes
17. $x^2 + 4x + 9, \ -13$
19. ± 18
21. $(x+1)(x+2)(x-2), \ -2, -2, 2$

Rational Zeros Theorem

Let $P(x) = a_n x^n + a_{n-1} x^{n-1} + \ldots + a_1 x + a_0$, $\quad a_n \neq 0$ be a polynomial with integer coefficients.

If p/q is a zero of $P(x)$:

then p is a factor of the constant term $\quad a_0$

and q is a factor of the leading coefficient $\quad a_n$

Example 7: Given $f(x) = 2x^4 - 11x^3 + 14x^2 - 11x + 12$. Find all rational zeros.

Solution: If p/q is a rational zero of the function, by the rational zeros theorem p must be a factor of $a_0 = 12$ and q must be a factor of $a_4 = 2$.

The possible values of p are: $\quad \pm 1, \pm 2, \pm 3, \pm 4, \pm 6$ or ± 12

The possible values of q are: $\quad \pm 1$ or ± 2.

The possible rational zeros are found by forming all possible quotients of the form p/q:

$$\pm 1, \quad \pm 1/2, \quad \pm 2, \quad \pm 3, \quad \pm 3/2, \quad \pm 4, \quad \pm 6, \text{ or } \pm 12$$

We do not know if any of these numbers are zeros, but if $f(x)$ has any rational zeros, they will be in this list.

The proposed zeros can be tested using synthetic division.

Doing so, we find that 4 is a zero:

$$
\begin{array}{r|rrrrr}
4 & 2 & -11 & 14 & -11 & 12 \\
  &   & 8   & -12 & 8   & -12 \\
\hline
  & 2 & -3 & 2   & -3 & 0
\end{array}
\qquad \text{remainder is } 0
$$

We can now look for zeros of the simpler polynomial we find with synthetic division.

$$Q(x) = 2x^3 - 3x^2 + 2x - 3$$

Any rational zero of $Q(x)$ will have a numerator of $\pm 3, \pm 1$ and a denominator of $\pm 2, \pm 1$

Thus, any rational zeros of $Q(x)$ will be:

$\pm 3, \ \pm 3/2, \ \pm 1, \ \pm 1/2$

Again using synthetic division and trial and error we find that 3/2 is a zero

$$
\begin{array}{r|rrrr}
3/2 & 2 & -3 & 2 & -3 \\
    &   & 3 & 0 & 3 \\
\hline
    & 2 & 0 & 2 & 0
\end{array}
\qquad \text{remainder is 0}
$$

The quotient is $2x^2 + 2$, which, by the quadratic formula, has i and $-i$ as zeros. These are imaginary zeros. The real zeros of the function are:

4 and 3/2

In a problem like Example 7, you can use a graphing calculator to graph the function and see if any of the zeros of the graph are close to the possible zeros.

Test these zeros first using synthetic division.

See Chapter 6, Example 25 to find real zeros using a graphing calculator.

Descartes' Rule of Signs, stated below, gives a useful test for finding the number of positive or negative real zeros of a given polynomial.

The function to be tested must be written in **descending or ascending order**.

164

Decartes' Rule of Signs:

If $f(x)$ is a polynomial function with real coefficients:

a. The number of positive real zeros of $f(x)$ is either equal to the number of variations that occur in the signs of the coefficients of $f(x)$, or is less than the number of variations by a positive even integer.

b. The number of negative real zeros of $f(x)$ is either equal to the number of variations in the signs of the coefficients of $f(-x)$, or is less than the number of variations by a positive even integer.

Section 3.4 Exercises

Find a polynomial function of degree 3 with the given numbers as zeros.

1. $-1, 3, 5$

2. $-3, 4i, -4i$

3. $4, i, -i$

4. $\sqrt{3}, -\sqrt{3}, 3$

5. $1+\sqrt{2}, 1-\sqrt{2}, -4$

6. $2+5i, 2-5i, -3$

7. $-2, 0, 3$

8. $-1/2, 0, 3/2$

9. Find a polynomial function of degree 5 with -2 as a zero of multiplicity 3, 0 as a zero of multiplicity 1, and 2 as a zero of multiplicity 1.

10. Find a polynomial of degree 4 with -1 as a zero of multiplicity 1, 4 as a zero of multiplicity 2, and -2 as a zero of multiplicity 1.

Suppose that a polynomial function of degree 4 with rational coefficients has the given numbers as zeros. Find the other zeros.

11. $-2, \sqrt{3}, 4$

12. $-2i, 3, -\sqrt{5}$

13. $2i, 0, -4$

14. $-2-i, 2-\sqrt{5}$

Suppose that a polynomial function of degree 5 with rational coefficients has the given numbers as zeros. Find the other zeros.

15. $-1/2, \sqrt{3}, -2i$

16. $-3, 0, 3, -2i$

Find a polynomial function of lowest degree with rational coefficients that has the given numbers as some of its zeros.

17. $2+i, 3$

18. $-3i, 2$

19. $\sqrt{2}, -3i$

20. $\sqrt{3}, -i$

List all possible rational zeros of the function:

21. $4x^5 - x^3 + 2$

22. $4x^3 - 3x^2 + 4x - 8$

Find the rational zeros and then the other zeros:

23. $f(x) = x^3 - 8x^2 + 17x - 4$

24. $f(x) = 12x^3 + 20x^2 - x - 6$

25. $f(x) = x^4 + 2x^3 - 13x^2 - 38x - 24$

Section 3.5   Rational Functions

Rational Function:

A rational function is a function of the form

$$f(x) = \frac{p(x)}{q(x)}$$
where $p(x)$ and $q(x)$ are polynomials and

$$q(x) \neq 0$$

Since any values of x such that $q(x) = 0$ cannot be part of the domain of the function, a rational function usually has one or more breaks in it.

Examples of rational functions:

The simplest rational function is $f(x) = \dfrac{1}{x}$ where $x \neq 0$

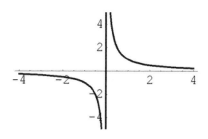

The domain of this function is the set of all real numbers except 0. Notice that f is an odd function, and thus the graph is symmetric with respect to the origin.

$f(x) = \dfrac{1}{x^2}$ where $x \neq 0$

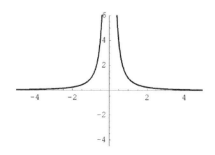

Look at the graph of $f(x) = \dfrac{x+1}{2x^2 + 5x - 3}$

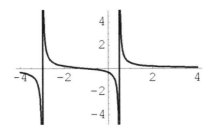

In these graphs the vertical lines seen on the graph are asymptotes, and not actually part of the graph.

$f(x) = \dfrac{x+3}{x-2}$

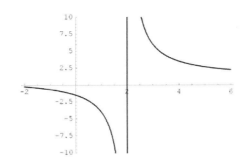

$f(x) = \dfrac{3x^2 - 3x - 6}{x^2 + 8x + 16}$

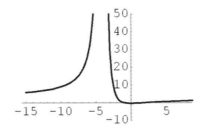

$$f(x) = \frac{x^2}{x+2}$$

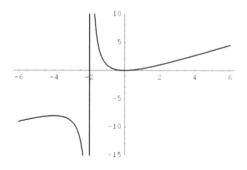

Finding the Domain of a Rational Function

Example 1: Given: $f(x) = \dfrac{1}{x-4}$

Find the domain and draw the graph.

Solution: When finding the domain, remember that the function is undefined when the denominator equals zero. To find the domain, set the denominator equal to zero and solve. The result **cannot** be in the domain.

$$x - 4 = 0$$

$$x = 4 \qquad\qquad \text{this value causes the function to be undefined}$$

Thus, the domain cannot include 4 and is:

$$(-\infty, 4) \cup (4, \infty)$$

To graph the function, notice that the function is the graph of

$$f(x) = \frac{1}{x} \qquad \text{shifted to the right 4 units.}$$

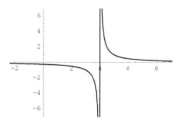

See Chapter 6, Example 26 for this problem solved with a graphing calculator.

Example 2: Look back at the graphs shown at the start of this section. What is the domain of each of these functions?

Solution:

$$f(x) = \frac{1}{x}$$ Domain: $(-\infty, 0) \cup (0, \infty)$

$$f(x) = \frac{1}{x^2}$$ Domain: $(-\infty, 0) \cup (0, \infty)$

$$f(x) = \frac{x+1}{2x^2 + 5x - 3}$$ Domain: $(-\infty, -3) \cup (-3, 1/2) \cup (1/2, \infty)$

$$f(x) = \frac{x+3}{x-2}$$ Domain: $(-\infty, 2) \cup (2, \infty)$

$$f(x) = \frac{3x^2 - 3x - 6}{x^2 + 8x + 16}$$ Domain: $(-\infty, -4) \cup (-4, \infty)$

$$f(x) = \frac{x^2}{x+2}$$ Domain: $(-\infty, -2) \cup (-2, \infty)$

Asymptotes

For the rational function $y = f(x)$

    If $\left| f(x) \right| \to \infty$ as $x \to a$
        then the line $x = a$ is a <u>vertical asymptote.</u>

    If $f(x) \to a$ as $\left| x \right| \to \infty$
        then the line $y = a$ is a <u>horizontal asymptote.</u>

To Find Vertical Asymptotes:

    set the denominator equal to 0 and solve for x.

If a is a zero of the denominator, then the line $x = a$ is a vertical asymptote.

Example 3: Find the vertical asymptotes for the graph of each of the following:

a. $f(x) = \dfrac{4x}{x^2 + 2x - 15}$ b. $f(x) = \dfrac{x + 3}{x^3 - 2x}$

Solution:

a. $f(x) = \dfrac{4x}{x^2 + 2x - 15}$

We set the denominator $= 0$ and solve for x to find the zeros of the denominator

$$x^2 + 2x - 15 = 0$$

$$(x + 5)(x - 3) = 0$$

The zeros of the denominator are: $-5, \ 3$.

The vertical asymptotes are: $x = -5$ and $x = 3$

172

b. $f(x) = \dfrac{x+3}{x^3 - 2x}$

Again, set the denominator = 0 to find the zeros of the denominator:

$$x^3 - 2x = 0$$

$$x(x^2 - 2) = 0$$

The zeros of the denominator are: $0, \ \sqrt{2}, \ -\sqrt{2}$

The vertical asymptotes are: $x = 0; \ x = \sqrt{2}; \ x = -\sqrt{2}$

To Find Horizontal Asymptotes:

a. If the numerator has a lower degree than the denominator, there is a horizontal asymptote at:

$$y = 0$$

b. If the numerator and the denominator have the same degree, use the coefficients of each to form a fraction: $\dfrac{a_n}{b_n}$

there is a vertical asymptote at:

$$y = \dfrac{a_n}{b_n}$$

If the degree of the numerator is greater than the degree of the denominator there is <u>no horizontal asymptote</u>.

Example 4: Find the horizontal asymptotes for the graph of each of the following:

a. $f(x) = \dfrac{2x - 6}{x^3 - 1}$

b. $f(x) = \dfrac{2x^2 + 1}{3x^2 - 1}$

173

Solution:

a. $f(x) = \dfrac{2x - 6}{x^3 - 1}$

The degree of the numerator is 1 and is lower than the degree of the denominator which is 3. Therefore there is a horizontal asymptote at $y = 0$.

b. $f(x) = \dfrac{2x^2 + 1}{3x^2 - 1}$

Since the numerator and denominator both have a degree of 2, form a fraction using the coefficients of the highest degreed term in each: 2/3.
Therefore there is a horizontal asymptote at $y = 2/3$.

Facts about Asymptotes:

Vertical asymptotes occur at the x-values of the zeros of the denominator.

The graph never crosses a vertical asymptote.

The line $y = 0$ (the x-axis) is a horizontal asymptote when the degree of the numerator is less than the degree of the denominator.

When the degree of the numerator and denominator are the same, the line

$$y = \frac{coefficient\ of\ numertor}{coefficient\ of\ deno\min ator} \qquad \text{is a horizontal asymptote}$$

A graph may cross a horizontal asymptote but does not always do so.

An oblique asymptote occurs when the degree of the numerator is 1 greater than the degree of the denominator.

Example 5.   Find all asymptotes of $f(x) = \dfrac{x^2 + 1}{x - 3}$

Solution: From the denominator we see that 3 is a zero of the denominator and thus, $x = 3$ is a vertical asymptote.

The degree of the numerator is 1 more than the degree of the denominator. We will look for an oblique asymptote:

Using synthetic division:

$$f(x) = \frac{x^2 + 1}{x - 3} = x + 3 + \frac{10}{x - 3}$$

As x gets very large, the remainder fraction is very small, and the graph will approach the line

$$y = x + 3 \qquad \text{this is an oblique asymptote}$$

The graph of Example 5 is:

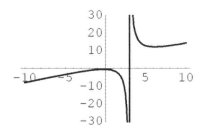

Remember that the vertical line on the graph is the vertical asymptote at $x = 3$.

Example 6: Given: $f(x) = \dfrac{3x^2 - 2x - 1}{x - 3}$ Find all asymptotes.

Solution: From the denominator, the line $x = 3$ is a vertical asymptote.

Use the degrees of the numerator and denominator to find other asymptotes:

The degree of the numerator is 1 greater than the degree of the denominator.

Check for oblique asymptote using division:

$$\frac{3x^2 - 2x - 1}{x - 3} = 3x + 4 + \frac{7}{x - 3}$$

$y = 3x + 4$ is an oblique asymptote.

Graph:

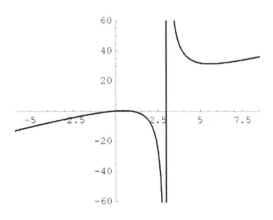

Notice the two asymptotes in the graph.:

Horizontal Asymptote: $x = 3$

Oblique Asymptote: $y = 3x + 4$

Steps for Graphing Rational Functions:

1. Find any vertical asymptotes using the zeros of the denominator.
   Sketch any asymptotes found.

2. Determine any other asymptotes: either horizontal or oblique.
   Sketch any asymptotes found.

3. Find any intercepts.
   for the x-intercepts, let $y = 0$
                    and
   for the y-intercept, let $x = 0$.

4. Plot a few selected points ….. at least one in each region of the
   domain determined by any vertical asymptotes.

5. Draw the graph.

Section 3.5 Exercises

Find any vertical, horizontal, or oblique asymptotes for the following:

1. $f(x) = \dfrac{2}{x-4}$

2. $f(x) = \dfrac{-3}{x+1}$

3. $f(x) = \dfrac{x+3}{x-2}$

4. $f(x) = \dfrac{x-5}{2-x}$

5. $f(x) = \dfrac{4x+5}{5x-3}$

6. $f(x) = \dfrac{5x}{x-2}$

7. $f(x) = \dfrac{3}{x^2-4}$

8. $f(x) = \dfrac{-2}{x^2-x-6}$

9. $f(x) = \dfrac{x^2-3}{x+1}$

10. $f(x) = \dfrac{x^2+9}{x-1}$

11. $f(x) = \dfrac{(x-1)(x+3)}{(x-2)(3x-1)}$

12. $f(x) = \dfrac{2(x+1)(x-4)}{(4x-2)(x+2)}$

13. $f(x) = \dfrac{2x^2-4}{x^2+1}$

14. $f(x) = \dfrac{-4x^2+12}{x^2+4}$

Sketch the graph of the following:

15. $f(x) = \dfrac{3}{4+x}$

16. $f(x) = -\dfrac{6}{x^2}$

17. $f(x) = \dfrac{1}{x^2+2}$

18. $f(x) = \dfrac{x+1}{x-2}$

19. $f(x) = \dfrac{2x}{x^2+3x+2}$

20. $f(x) = \dfrac{x-2}{x^2-4x+3}$

Find a rational function that satisfies the given conditions. Answers many vary.

e21. Vertical asymptotes $x = -3, x = 2$

22. Vertical asymptotes $x = -2, x = 3$; horizontal asymptote: $y = 4/3$; x-intercept $(1, 0)$

Section 3.6   Polynomial and Rational Inequalities

Quadratic Inequality:

A quadratic inequality is an inequality that can be written in the form

$$ax^2 + bx + c < 0$$

for real numbers $a \neq 0$, b, and c.

The symbol $<$ can be replaced with $>$, $\leq$, or $\geq$.

Examples of quadratic inequalities:

$$3x^2 - 2x + 4 > 0 \qquad\qquad -x^2 + 4x \leq 7 \qquad\qquad -4x^2 > 12$$

Quadratic inequalities are one type of polynomial inequalities. Other examples of polynomial inequalities are:

$$3x > 2 \qquad\qquad 2x^4 + 2x^2 - x \leq 9 \qquad\qquad x^3 + 2x^2 > x - 3$$

If the inequality sign is replaced with an equal sign, the result is an equation.   When this equation is solved, the results help in finding the solutions to the inequality.

Example 1:   Solve: $x^3 - 4x > 0$

Solution: In this problem we are looking for all values of x which make the given polynomial greater than zero. This means that we are looking for intervals where the graph of the function $f(x) = x^3 - 4x$ has POSITIVE values.

We begin by finding the zeros of the function.

$$x^3 - 4x = 0$$

$$x(x^2 - 4) = 0$$

$$x(x - 2)(x + 2) = 0$$

The zeros are -2, 0, and 2.

Remember that when the graph passes through the zeros the sign changes.

The zeros divide the x-axis into 4 intervals:

$$(-\infty,-2), \qquad (-2,0), \qquad (0,2), \qquad \text{and} \quad (2,\infty)$$

These intervals formed by the zeros are used to solve the problem. We will choose a test value within each interval and determine the sign of the function for each test value.

INTERVAL	TEST VALUE	SIGN OF $f(x)$
$(-\infty,-2)$	$f(-4)=-48$	negative
$(-2,0)$	$f(-1)=3$	positive
$(0,2)$	$f(1)=-3$	negative
$(2,\infty)$	$f(4)=48$	positive

The original problem was to solve: $\ x^3-4x>0$

Since the inequality sign says "polynomial" >0, the problem asks for those intervals where the polynomial is positive. From our intervals, we find two intervals where the values are positive. The solution is:

$$(-2,0) \cup (2,\infty)$$

Looking at the graph of $\ f(x)=x^3-4x$,

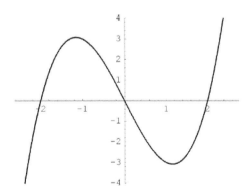

we see that the graph is positive when it is above the x-axis: between x values of -2 to 0 and also from values greater than 2. Thus the solution is $\ (-2,0) \cup (2,\infty)$.

The problem in Example 1 can be solved using a graphing calculator. See Chapter 6, Example 27.

To solve a polynomial inequality:

1. Use addition/subtraction to get a zero on one side of the inequality.

2. Replace the inequality symbol with an $=$ to find the zeros.

3. Use the solutions to divide the x-axis into intervals.

4. Choose a test value in each interval and determine the sign.

5. Pick the intervals that make the inequality symbol a true statement.

6. Include the endpoints of the intervals in the solution if the inequality symbol is $\geq$ or $\leq$.

Example 2:   Solve $2x^4 - 3x^3 - 5x^2 \leq -x - 1$

Solution:

In order to solve the inequality, we need to have zero on the right side of the inequality. We will add $x + 1$ to both sides:

$$2x^4 - 3x^3 - 5x^2 + x + 1 \leq 0$$

We begin by finding the zeros of $f(x) = 2x^4 - 3x^3 - 5x^2 + x + 1$

$$2x^4 - 3x^3 - 5x^2 + x + 1 = 0$$

Using synthetic division and the quadratic formula, we find that the zeros are:

$$-1, \quad 1 - \sqrt{2}, \quad 1/2, \quad 1 + \sqrt{2}$$

We find five intervals to be tested:

$$(-\infty,-1) \quad (-1,1-\sqrt{2}), \quad (1-\sqrt{2},1/2) \quad (1/2,1+\sqrt{2}), \quad (1+\sqrt{2},\infty)$$

INTERVAL	TEST VALUE	SIGN OF $f(x)$
$(-\infty,-1)$	$f(-3)=196$	positive
$(-1,1-\sqrt{2})$	$f(-1/2)=-1/4$	negative
$(1-\sqrt{2},1/2)$	$f(0)=1$	positive
$(1/2,1+\sqrt{2})$	$f(1)=-4$	negative
$(1+\sqrt{2},\infty)$	$f(5)=756$	positive

Two intervals are negative and are the solution to the inequality:

$$[-1,1-\sqrt{2}]\cup[1/2,1+\sqrt{2}]$$

To solve Example 2 using a graphing calculator, see Chapter 6, Example 28.

Rational Inequalities:

Inequalities that contain rational expressions are called rational inequalities.

Example 3: Solve $\dfrac{x-2}{x+2} \geq \dfrac{x+3}{x-1}$

Solution: Begin by subtracting $\dfrac{x+3}{x-1}$ from both sides so that the right side is zero.

$$\frac{x-2}{x+2}-\frac{x+3}{x-1} \geq 0 \qquad \text{Multiply both sides by LCD}$$

$$(x+2)(x-1)\left(\frac{x-2}{x+2}\right)-(x+2)(x-1)\left(\frac{x+3}{x-1}\right) \geq (x+2)(x-1)(0)$$

181

Find the zeros:

$$(x-1)(x-2)-(x+2)(x+3)=0 \qquad \text{Simplify}$$

$$x^2-3x+2-(x^2+5x+6)=0$$

$$x^2-3x+2-x^2-5x-6=0$$

$$-8x-4=0$$

$$-8x=4$$

$$x=-1/2$$

The critical values are -2, $-1/2$, and 1.

The -2 and $-1/2$ come from the values that make the denominators equal zero.

The intervals would be:

$$(-\infty,-2) \qquad (-2,-1/2) \qquad (-1/2,1) \qquad and \qquad (1,\infty)$$

INTERVAL	TEST VALUE	SIGN OF $f(x)$
$(-\infty,-2)$	$f(-4)=2.8$	positive
$(-2,-1/2)$	$f(-1)=-2$	negative
$(-1/2,1)$	$f(0)=2$	positive
$(1,\infty)$	$f(3)=-2.8$	negative

The solution is the two positive valued intervals: $(-\infty,-2)\cup[-1/2,1)$. The zero of -1 is included in the solution interval because of the symbol $\geq$ in the problem .

To solve Example 3 using a graphing calculator, see Chapter 6, Example 29.

To solve a rational inequality:

1. Use addition/subtraction to get zero on one side of the equation.

2. Replace the inequality symbol with an = to find the zeros.

3. Find the undefined values for the variable (found in the denominators).

4. The critical values are the zeros and the undefined values.

5. Use the critical values to divide the x-axis into intervals.

6. Choose a test value in each interval and determine the sign.

7. Pick the intervals that make the inequality symbol a true statement.

8. If the inequality symbol is $\leq$ or $\geq$ the zeros should be included in the interval.

Section 3.6 Exercises

Given: $f(x) = x^2 + 3x - 18$ Solve each:

1. $f(x) = 0$

2. $f(x) > 0$

3. $f(x) \geq 0$

4. $f(x) \leq 0$

5. $f(x) < 0$

6. $f(x) > 0$

Solve:

7. $(x+1)(x-2) > 0$

8. $(x-5)(x-3) \leq 0$

9. $x^2 - x - 12 > 0$

10. $x^2 - x - 12 \leq 0$

11. $x^2 > 36$

12. $x^2 < 4$

13. $x^2 + 6x + 16 < 8$

14. $2x^2 - 9x > -4$

15. $x^3 - 5x \leq 0$

16. $x^3 - 16x \geq 0$

17. $\dfrac{x-3}{x+6} \leq 0$

18. $\dfrac{x+1}{x-3} > 0$

19. $\dfrac{4}{x+1} < \dfrac{2}{x+3}$

20. $\dfrac{x+3}{x-5} \leq 1$

Chapter 3 Summary

Polynomial Function:

$$f(x) = a_n x^n + a_{n-1} x^{n-1} + \ldots\ldots + a_1 x + a_0$$

End Behavior:

The leading term of the polynomial functions demonstrates its end behavior.

<u>Degree Even:</u>

Leading Coefficient Positive: the end behavior approaches $+\infty$

Leading Coefficient Negative: end behavior approaches $-\infty$

<u>Degree Odd:</u>

Leading Coefficient Positive:

as x approaches $-\infty$, the end behavior approaches $-\infty$

as x approaches $+\infty$, the end behavior approaches $+\infty$

Leading Coefficient Negative:

as x approaches $-\infty$, the end behavior approaches $+\infty$

as x approaches $+\infty$, the end behavior approaches $-\infty$

The Intermediate Value Theorem:

If $P(x)$ is a polynomial function with only real coefficients, and if for real numbers a and b, $P(a)$ and $P(b)$ are opposite in sign, then there exists at least one real zero between a and b

Division of Polynomials:

For any polynomial $P(x)$ and any number k, there exists a unique polynomial $Q(x)$ and number r such that:

$$P(x) \quad = \quad (x-k) \quad * \quad Q(x) \qquad + \quad r$$

The Remainder Theorem:

If $P(x)$ is divided by $(x-k)$, then the remainder is $P(k)$.

The Factor Theorem:

The polynomial $(x-k)$ is a factor of the polynomial $P(x)$ if $P(k) = 0$.

Fundamental Theorem of Algebra:
Every polynomial of degree 1 or more has at least one complex zero.
$$P(x) = (x - k) * Q(x)$$

Conjugate Zeros Theorem
If $P(x)$ is a polynomial having <u>only real coefficients</u> and if
$a + bi$ is a zero of $P(x)$,
then the conjugate
$a - bi$ is also a zero of $P(x)$.

If $P(x)$ is a polynomial having <u>only rational coefficients</u> and if
$a + b\sqrt{c}$ is a zero of $P(x)$,
then the conjugate
$a - b\sqrt{c}$ is also a zero of $P(x)$.

Rational Zeros Theorem
Let $P(x) = a_n x^n + a_{n-1} x^{n-1} + \ldots + a_1 x + a_0, \quad a_n \neq 0$ be a
polynomial with integer coefficients.
If p/q is a zero of $P(x)$:
        then p is a factor of the constant term a_0
        and q is a factor of the leading coefficient a_n

Decartes' Rule of Signs:
If $f(x)$ is a polynomial function with real coefficients:
a. The number of positive real zeros of $f(x)$ is either equal to the number of variations that occur in the coefficients of $f(x)$, or is less than the number of variations by a positive even integer.
b. The number of negative real zeros of $f(x)$ is either equal to the number of variations of $f(-x)$, or is less than the number of variations by a positive even integer.

<u>Rational Function</u>:
A function of the form
$$f(x) = \frac{p(x)}{q(x)}$$
where $p(x)$ and $q(x)$ are polynomials and $q(x) \neq 0$

Asymptotes:
For the rational function $y = f(x)$
If $\left| f(x) \right| \to \infty$ as $x \to a$

then the line $x = a$ is a <u>vertical asymptote.</u>

If $f(x) \rightarrow a$ as $|x| \rightarrow \infty$

then the line $y = a$ is a <u>horizontal asymptote.</u>

Graphing Rational Functions:
1. Find any vertical asymptotes using the zeros of the denominator. Sketch any asymptotes found.
2. Determine any other asymptotes: either horizontal or oblique. Sketch any asymptotes found.
3. Find any intercepts.
   For x-intercepts, let $y = 0$ and
   for y-intercept, let $x = 0$.
4. Plot a few selected points ….. at least one in each region of the domain determined by any vertical asymptotes.
5. Draw the graph.

To solve a polynomial inequality:
1. Use addition/subtraction to get zero on one side of the equation.
2. Replace the inequality symbol with an = to find the zeros.
3. Use the solutions to divide the x-axis into intervals.
4. Choose a test value in each interval and determine the sign.
5. Pick the intervals that make the inequality symbol a true statement.
6. Include the endpoints of the intervals in the solution if the inequality symbol is $\geq$ or $\leq$.

To solve a rational inequality:
1. Use addition/subtraction to get 0 on one side.
2. Replace the inequality symbol with an = and find the zeros.
3. Find the undefined values for the variable (found in the denominators).
4. The critical values are the zeros and the undefined values.
5. Use the critical values to divide the x-axis into intervals.
6. Choose a test value in each interval and determine the sign.
7. Pick the intervals that make the inequality symbol a true statement.
8. If the inequality symbol is $\leq$ or $\geq$ the zeros should be included in the interval.

Chapter 3 Review

Find the zeros, relative maxima, relative minima, and the domain and range.:

1. $f(x) = x^2 - 4$

2. $f(x) = x^3 + 3x^2 - 4x - 12$

3. $f(x) = x^4 - 2x^3 - 8x^2$

Classify the function as constant, linear, quadratic, cubic, or quartic. Find the leading term, the leading coefficient, and the degree.

4. $f(x) = 2 + 5x - 7x^3$ 5. $f(x) = 3x - 37x^4$

6. $f(x) = 17x - 2$ 7. $f(x) = 4$

8. $f(x) = 2x - 12 + 3x^2$

Describe the end behavior of the graph of the function.

9. $f(x) = 7x^5 - 12x$ 10. $f(x) = -6x^8 + 1$

Find the zeros and the multiplicity of each.

11. $f(x) = (x-2)^3 (x)(x+2)^2$

12. $f(x) = x^4 - 10x^2 + 9$

13. $f(x) = x^3 + 3x^2 - 25x - 75$

Use the intermediate value theorem to decide if possible whether the function has a zero between the two given values.

14. $f(x) = 4x^2 - 8x - 3$; -2 and 0 15. $f(x) = 2x^3 - 6$; 2 and 3

Use synthetic division to find the quotient and the remainder

16. $(x^3 + 3x^2 - 12x + 4) \div (x-3)$ 17. $(x^4 - 16) \div (x-2)$

Use synthetic division to decide if the given numbers are zeros.

18. $1, -2$; $f(x) = x^3 - 3x^2 - 6x + 8$

19. $-\sqrt{2}, 3$; $4x^2 - 8$

Factor the polynomial and then solve the equation $f(x) = 0$.

20. $f(x) = x^4 + 5x^2 - 36$

21. $f(x) = x^3 + x + 3x^2 + 3$

Find a polynomial of lowest degree with rational coefficients with the given numbers as some of the zeros.

22. $\sqrt{5}$

23. $i, -2$

Solve each of the following.

24. $x^2 - 25 < 0$

25. $x^2 > 6x - 9$

26. $\dfrac{x-3}{x+1} < 0$

CHAPTER 4

EXPONENTIAL AND LOGARITHMIC FUNCTIONS

Section 4.1 Inverses of Functions

Certain arithmetic operations are inverse operations. If we start with a number x, add 4 to our number, and then subtract 4, the result is our original number x. These operations of addition and subtraction are inverse operations. Sometimes we can find the inverse function of a given function as well.

This section will show how to start with a given function and obtain the inverse of the function if that inverse exists. If we can go from the output of a function back to its input, we have an inverse relation. If this relation is a function, then we have an inverse function.

Let's look at a simple relation g that consists of ordered pairs:

$$g = \{(-3,3),(-2,5),(0,9)\}$$

If we switch the values of the first and second coordinates, the relation we find is called the **inverse** of the relation g and would be:

$$\text{Inverse of } g = \{(3,-3),\ (5,-2),(9,0)\}$$

Inverse Relation of Ordered Pairs:

> The inverse of a relation of ordered pairs is found by interchanging the first and second coordinates of each ordered pair in the relation.

Example 1: Given the relation h: $h = \{(4,7),(1,6),(0,3)\}$
Find the inverse relation.

Solution: We find the inverse relation, by interchanging the coordinates of the ordered pairs.

$$\text{Inverse relation} = \{(7,4),(6,1),(3,0)\}$$

If we plot the three original points and then plot the three inverse points, we will see that the pairs in the inverse are reflections of the original points across the line $y = x$.

Example 2: Find an inverse equation for the equation:

$$y = x^2 - 3x$$

Solution: Interchange the variables x and y.

$$x = y^2 - 3y$$

Look at the graphs of the two equations in Example 2:

Original equation: Inverse equation

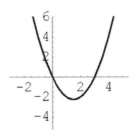   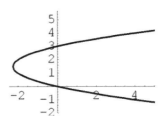

Combining these two graphs on one axis we see that the graph of the given equation and its inverse are reflections across the line $y = x$.

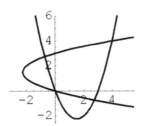

One-to-One Functions

For the function $y = 3x - 4$, two different values of x give results of two different values for y.

In contrast, for the function $y = x^2$, two different values of x can result in the same value of y. For example, $x = 4$ and $x = -4$ give the same result of 16.

A function like $y = 3x - 4$, where different elements from the domain lead to different elements in the range is called a **one-to-one function**.

One-to-one Function:

A function f is one-to-one if, for elements a and b from the domain of f,

$$a \neq b \text{ implies } f(a) \neq f(b).$$

The definition says that a function is one-to-one if the output values are different when the input values are different.

Inverse of a function:

If the inverse of a function is ALSO a function, it is called "f inverse" and

symbolically is written as:

$$f^{-1}$$

Note: this is not an exponent.

Example 3. Decide whether or not the following function is one-to-one:

$$f(x) = 2x - 4$$

Solution: Suppose that $a \neq b$. Then $2a \neq 2b$ and $2a - 4 \neq 2b - 4$ and since $a \neq b$ implies that $f(a) \neq f(b)$, then we know that f is one-to-one.

One-to-one Functions and their Inverses:

If a function is one-to-one, then its inverse is also a function.

The <u>domain</u> of a one-to-one function f is the <u>range</u> of its inverse f^{-1}.

The <u>range</u> of a one-to-one function f is the <u>domain</u> of its inverse f^{-1}.

Increasing and Decreasing functions are one-to-one.

Example 4. Given the function $f(x) = -2x + 6$. Prove that f is one-to-one.

Solution: We will make a formal proof to prove that f is one-to-one. We will assume that $f(a) = f(b)$ and then show that $a = b$.

$$f(a) = -2a + 6 \qquad \text{and} \qquad f(b) = -2b + 6$$

Since we assume these are equal, we will set them equal to begin.

$$-2a + 6 = -2b + 6$$

$$-2a = -2b \qquad\qquad \text{Subtract 6 from both sides}$$

$$a = b \qquad\qquad \text{Divide by negative 2}$$

Thus, since the assumption $f(a) = f(b)$ resulted in $a = b$, we have proved that the function f is one-to-one.

One way to show that a function is **not** one-to-one, is to find a pair of unequal input values that result in the same function output value.

Example 5. Given $f(x) = \sqrt{25 - x^2}$. Show that this function is not one-to-one.

Solution: We will look for a two different values of x that result in the same function value:

$$f(4) = \sqrt{25 - 4^2} = \sqrt{25 - 16} = \sqrt{9} = 3$$
$$f(-4) = \sqrt{25 - (-4)^2} = \sqrt{25 - 16} = \sqrt{9} = 3 \qquad \text{and } f \text{ is not one-to-one.}$$

195

Horizontal Line Test:

If every horizontal line cuts the graph of a function in no more than one point, then the function is one-to-one.

Use the horizontal line test to determine if a function is one-to-one.

A graphing calculator can be used to determine whether a function is one-to-one. See Chapter 6, Example 30.

How to Find an Inverse:
If a function f is one-to-one, the inverse can be found by these steps:

1. Replace $f(x)$ with y

2. Interchange x and y

3. Solve for y

4. Replace y with f^{-1}

Example 6: Given a one-to-one function $f(x) = 2x - 6$. Find the inverse.

Solution: Given $f(x) = 2x - 6$

$$y = 2x - 6 \qquad \text{replace } f(x) \text{ with } y$$

$$x = 2y - 6 \qquad \text{interchange } x \text{ and } y$$

$$x + 6 = 2y \qquad \text{solve for y}$$

$$\frac{x+6}{2} = y$$

$$f^{-1}(x) = \frac{x+6}{2}$$

Example 7. Given $f(x) = x^3$

    a. Determine whether f is one-to-one

    b. If it is one-to-one, find the inverse

Solution:

    a. We know that the graph of $f(x) = x^3$ is:

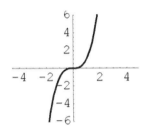

        The function is one-to-one because it passes the horizontal graph test.

    b. $f(x) = x^3$

        $y = x^3$ Replace $f(x)$ with y

        $x = y^3$ Interchange x and y

        $y = \sqrt[3]{x}$ Solve for y

        $f^{-1}(x) = \sqrt[3]{x}$

Composition of a Function and its Inverse:

If a function f is one-to-one, then f^{-1} is the inverse and:

    $(f^{-1} \circ f)(x) = f^{-1}(f(x)) = x$ for any x in the domain of f

        and

    $(f \circ f^{-1})(x) = f(f^{-1}(x)) = x$ for any x in the domain of f^{-1}

Example 8. Given $f(x) = 3x + 7$ and $f^{-1}(x) = \dfrac{x-7}{3}$. Use composition of functions to show that f^{-1} is the inverse of f.

Solution: Find $(f^{-1} \circ f)(x)$ and $(f \circ f^{-1})(x)$ and test if each is equal to x.

$$(f^{-1} \circ f)(x) = f^{-1}(f(x))$$
$$= f^{-1}(3x+7) = \frac{(3x+7)-7}{3} = \frac{3x}{3} = x$$

$$(f \circ f^{-1})(x) = f(f^{-1}(x))$$
$$= f\left(\frac{x-7}{3}\right) = 3\left(\frac{x-7}{3}\right) + 7 = x - 7 + 7 = x$$

Limiting the Domain

If the inverse of a function is not a function, in certain cases the domain of the given function can be reduced to allow the inverse to be a function.

Look at $y = x^2$: We know that this is the equation of a parabola and using the graph of a parabola with the horizontal line test, we find that it is not one-to-one. The graph is:

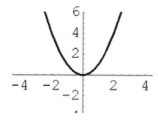

If we use only part of the domain, we will have a function as the inverse. If we limit the domain to be $[0, \infty)$, then the inverse becomes a function.

Look at the graphs of $f(x) = x^2, x \geq 0, and\ f^{-1} = \sqrt{x}$

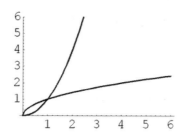   Note the reflection across the line $y = x$

198

Exercises 4.1

Find the inverse relation for:

1. $\{(5,4),(-2,3),(4,7)\}$
2. $\{(0,-2),(-3,-3),(-1,5)\}$

3. $y = 3x + 2$
4. $2x^2 + 3y^2 = 6$

5. $y = 2x^2 - 1x$
6. $x^4 y = 8$

7. $x = y^2 + 7y$
8. $x = 4y + 9$

Sketch the graph the equation, and then reflect the graph across the line $y = x$ to see the graph of the inverse.

9. $y = 2x - 1$
10. $y = x^2 + 3$

11. $x = -2y - 3$
12. $x = y^2$

Prove that the following functions are one-to-one.

13. $f(x) = 4x - 3$
14. $f(x) = x^3 + 2$

Show that the following functions are not one to one.

15. $f(x) = x^2 + 2$
16. $f(x) = x^4$

Use the horizontal line test to see which of the following are graphs of one-to-one functions:

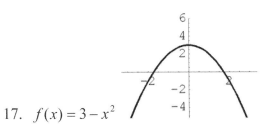

17. $f(x) = 3 - x^2$

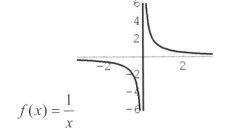

18. $f(x) = \dfrac{1}{x}$

19. $f(x) = \dfrac{1}{x^2}$

199

Graph the following by hand and determine if they are one-to-one functions.

20. $f(x) = 4x + 1$ 21. $f(x) = x^2 + 1$

Decide if the given function is one-to-one and if it is, find the inverse.

22. $f(x) = x^3 + 2$ 23. $f(x) = \dfrac{1}{x}$

24. $f(x) = x^2 - 3$ 25. $f(x) = 4x - 2$

26. $f(x) = 2 - x^2$, domain is $[0, \infty)$

Section 4.2 Exponential Functions

Properties of Exponents:

For $a > 0$, $a \neq 1$, and any real number x:

    1. a^x is a unique real number;

    2. $a^b = a^c$ if and only if $b = c$;

    3. if $a > 1$ and $m < n$ then $a^m < a^n$;

    4. if $0 < a < 1$ and $m < n$ then $a^m > a^n$.

We will now define an exponential function: $f(x) = a^x$

The domain of this function is the set of all real numbers

The function:
$$f(x) = a^x, \quad a > 0 \quad \text{and} \quad a \neq 1,$$

is the **exponential function** with base a.

Notice: if $a = 1$, the function is the constant function $f(x) = 1$.

From the properties above we see that an exponential function always has a positive base.

Graphs of the Exponential Function:

Look at the following two graphs showing exponential functions:

I. $f(x) = 2^x$

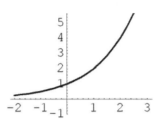

The base of the exponential function $f(x) = 2^x$ is 2. This graph is made by finding ordered pairs that satisfy the given function.

We see from the above graph that the function $f(x) = 2^x$ has a domain of all real numbers and a range of all positive numbers. The x-axis is a horizontal asymptote.

The graph of $f(x) = 2^x$ is **typical** of graphs of $f(x) = a^x$ where $a > 1$. For larger values of a the graphs rise more steeply, but the general shape is similar to the above graph.

Now look at a second exponential function:

II. $f(x) = (1/2)^x$

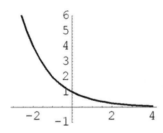

The base of the exponential function $f(x) = (1/2)^x$ is $1/2$. Looking at the graph, we can see that the domain is all real numbers, and the range is all positive numbers. The x-axis is a horizontal asymptote.

The graph of $f(x) = (1/2)^x$ is **typical** of graphs of $f(x) = a^x$ where $0 < a < 1$.

The graphs of $f(x) = 2^x$ and $f(x) = (1/2)^x$ are **mirror images** of each other with respect to the y-axis.

From the horizontal line test, we see that **<u>exponential functions are one-to-one</u>**.

To graph other types of exponential functions, we can use translations and reflections of the above graphs.

Example 1. Sketch the graph of the function $f(x) = 2^{x-4}$.

Solution: From our study of translations we know that the graph of this function is the graph of the function $f(x) = 2^x$ shifted **right 4 units.**

The graph would be:

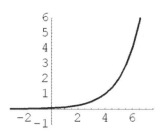

A graphing calculator can be used to verify your results.

Example 2. Sketch the graph of the function $f(x) = 2^x - 2$

Solution: From our study of translations we know that the graph of this function is the graph of the function $f(x) = 2^x$ shifted **down 2 units.**

The graph would be:

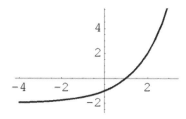

A graphing calculator can be used to verify your results.

Example 3.   Sketch the graph of the function $f(x) = 4 - 2^{-x}$

Solution: The graph of this function is the graph of the function $f(x) = 2^x$ **reflected across the y-axis, and then reflected across the x-axis and then shifted up 4 units.**

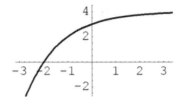

A graphing calculator can be used to verify the results.

One of the most useful exponential functions is the compound interest function.

Example 4:   Compound Interest

If P dollars is deposited into an account paying a rate of interest r compounded n times, then after t years the account will contain the amount given by the equation:

$$A = P\left(1 + \frac{r}{n}\right)^{nt}$$

If \$10,000 is deposited at 10% interest, compounded quarterly, define a function of time with the given money, compounding time, and interest. Then find the amount of money in the account at the end of 10 years.

Solution: $P = 10,000, \quad r = 10\% = 0.10, \quad n = 4$

$$A(t) = 10,000\left(1 + \frac{0.10}{4}\right)^{4t}$$

Now, for 10 years, let $t = 10$ in the defined function:

$$A(10) = 10,000\left(1 + \frac{0.10}{4}\right)^{4*10} = 10,000(1.025)^{40}$$

Using a calculator:

$$A(10) = \$26850.64$$

If the problem above had not given us the number of years and instead had given us the amount of money we hoped to earn and asked how many years it would take for the deposit to reach this amount, a graphing calculator can be used to solve this type of problem. See Chapter 6, Example 31.

Euler's Number: *e*

Let's look again at our compound interest formula

$$A = P\left(1 + \frac{r}{n}\right)^{nt}$$

Suppose we can find an investment that will pay 100% interest, so that $r = 1$.

However, with such a great rate, we are only able to invest \$1.00. P would also = 1

Also we can only invest for 1 year so t would = 1.

Our compound interest formula would be:

$$A = \left(1 + \frac{1}{n}\right)^{n}$$

Use this formula and let the compound number n increase to a large number and see what happens.

n	$\left(1+\dfrac{1}{n}\right)^{n}$
1	2
2	2.25
5	2.48832
10	2.59374
25	2.66584
50	2.69159
100	2.70481
500	2.71557
1,000	2.71692
10,000	2.71815
1,000,000	2.71828

Look at the table we calculated. The results imply that as n increases, the value of $(1+1/n)^{n}$ gets closer and closer to some number. The number each of our calculations is approaching is called e.

Euler's Number	$e = 2.718281828\ldots$

The number e is a non-repeating, non-terminating number.

Since e is a fixed number, we can raise it to the power of x.

The function $f(x) = e^{x}$ has the graph:

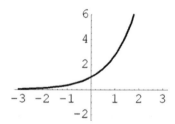

Remember that e is a number slightly larger than 2. Thus the graph looks very similar to the graph of $f(x) = 2^{x}$.

The function $f(x) = e^{-x}$ has the graph:

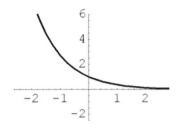

Example 5. Sketch the graph of the following. Describe how each graph can be obtained from the graph of $y = e^x$

    a. $f(x) = e^{-1/4x}$ b. $f(x) = 2 - e^{-3x}$ c. $f(x) = e^{x+1}$

Solution:

    a.   the graph of $f(x) = e^{-1/4x}$ is a horizontal stretch of the graph of $f(x) = e^x$ and then a reflection across the y-axis.

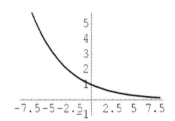

    b.   the graph of $f(x) = 2 - e^{-3x}$ is a horizontal shrinking of the graph of $f(x) = e^x$, then a reflection across the y-axis, and then across the x-axis and finally a translation up 2 units

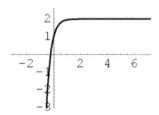

207

c. the graph of $f(x) = e^{x+1}$ is a translation of the graph of $f(x) = e^x$ to the left 1 unit

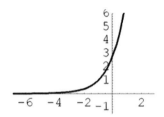

Section 4.2 Exercises

Use what you know about graphs of exponential functions to match the functions below with one of the graphs shown below.

1. $f(x) = 2^x - 2$

2. $f(x) = (1/2)^x + 2$

3. $f(x) = e^x + 1$

4. $f(x) = e^{x+2}$

5. $f(x) = 3^{-x} - 1$

6. $f(x) = -e^x$

a.

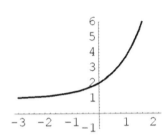

b.

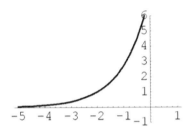

c.

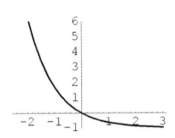

d.

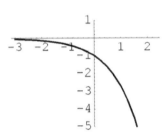

e.

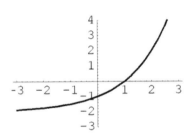

f.

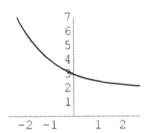

Sketch the graph of the following.

7. $f(x) = 2.5^x$

8. $f(x) = 5^x$

9. $f(x) = 2^{-x}$

10. $f(x) = (1/2)^x$

209

11. $f(x) = -3^x$

12. $f(x) = 2 - 2^x$

13. $f(x) = 2^x - 2$

14. $f(x) = 3^{x+1}$

15. $f(x) = 3^{x-1}$

16. $f(x) = 3^x + 1$

17. $f(x) = 3^x - 1$

18. $f(x) = e^x + 3$

19. $f(x) = e^x - 2$

20. $f(x) = e^{x+3}$

21. $f(x) = e^{x-2}$

22. $f(x) = -e^x$

23. $f(x) = e^{-x}$

Section 4.3   Logarithmic Functions

In Section 4.2 we learned that the exponential function $f(x) = a^x$, when $0 < a < 1$ or when $a > 1$, is a one-to-one function. Since the function is one-to-one, we realize that it will have an inverse. Next we will look at the inverse of the exponential function.

The inverse of the exponential function with base a is called the **logarithmic function with base a** and we symbolize this function as **$\log_a$.**

These values are written $\log_a(x)$ or $\log_a x$ and is read "the logarithm of x with base a".

Definition of $\log_a$

Let a be a positive real number different from 1. The logarithm of x with base a is defined by:

$$y = \log_a x \qquad \text{if and only if} \qquad x = a^y$$

for every $x > 0$ and every real number y.

The two equations in the definition are equivalent. Notice that the bases are the same.

The first form is called the **logarithmic form:** $\log_a x = y$

The second form is called the **exponential form:** $a^y = x$

Think of $\log_a x$ as: "the power to which we raise a to get x".

Example 1. Find the value of $y = \log_2(8)$.

 If we change from the logarithmic form to the exponential form, we get $2^y = 8$. We can easily solve this form of the equation for y since 2 raised to the power of 3 equals 8.

From our original equation, $y = \log_2(8)$, and the fact that we found y equivalent to 3, our equation in logarithmic form is:

$$\log_2(8) = 3$$

From Section 4.2, we saw that the graph of $y = a^x$ where $a > 1$ is:

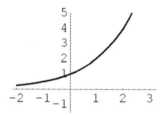

The domain is all real numbers, and the range is all positive real numbers. The graph is increasing and has a horizontal asymptote of the x-axis. The y-intercept is $(0,1)$ and there is no x-intercept.

Now let's examine the **graph of** $y = \log_a x$ where $a > 1$:

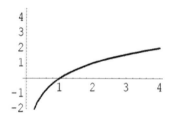

The domain is all positive numbers, and the range is all real numbers. The graph is increasing and has a vertical asymptote of the y-axis. The x-intercept is $(1, 0)$ and there is no y-intercept.

Since these two functions are inverses of each other, let's put the two graphs together, and we see:

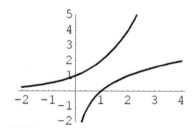

Remember that graphs of inverse functions are reflections across the line $y = x$.

Example 2: Find each of the following:

    a. $\log_{10}(1000)$ b. $\log_2 16$ c. $\log_{16} 4$

    d. $\log_7 1$ e. $\log_5 5$

Solution:

    a. The exponent to which we raise 10 to obtain 1,000 is 3.
$$\log_{10}(1000) = 3.$$

    b. The problem asks to what power we would raise the number 2 so that we get the number 16. We know that $2^4 = 16$
$$\log_2 16 = 4$$

    c. We know that $4 = \sqrt{16} = 16^{1/2}$. The exponent to which we would raise 16 so that we get 4 is 1/2.
$$\log_{16} 4 = 1/2$$

    d. What power would we raise 7 to so that we could get 1? We know that $7^0 = 1$.
$$\log_7 1 = 0$$

    e. The exponent that we would raise 5 to so that we get 5 is 1. $5^1 = 5$
$$\log_5 5 = 1$$

Conversions between Exponential Equations and Logarithmic Equations.

We have already seen that the logarithm of a number is often thought of as an exponent. Thus:

    the logarithm, base a, of a number x is the exponent to which a must be raised to equal the value of x

---

Conversion:

    $\log_a x = y$ is the same as $x = a^y$

1. The bases are the same in both forms.

2. The y in the log form becomes the exponent in the exponential form.

Example 3. Convert the following exponential equations to equivalent logarithmic equations.

    a. $27 = 3^x$ b. $10^{-2} = 0.01$ c. $e^m = 17$

Solution:

    a. $27 = 3^x$ $\rightarrow$ $\log_3 27 = x$

    b. $10^{-2} = 0.01$ $\rightarrow$ $\log_{10}(0.01) = -2$

    c. $e^m = 17$ $\rightarrow$ $\log_e 17 = m$

Example 4. Convert the following logarithmic equations to exponential equations.

    a. $\log_2 16 = 4$ b. $\log_a R = 6$ c. $x = \log_n P$

Solution:

    a. $\log_2 16 = 4$ $\rightarrow$ $2^4 = 16$

    b. $\log_a R = 6$ $\rightarrow$ $a^6 = R$

    c. $x = \log_n P$ $\rightarrow$ $n^x = P$

Common Logarithm

Common Logarithms are logarithms with a base of 10.

The symbol   log without a written base implies the common logarithm and the base is understood to be 10.

    $\log x$ is the same as $\log_{10} x$.

Chapter 6, Example 32 shows an example of a problem using a calculator to evaluate a common logarithm.

Natural Logarithms

> **Natural Logarithm:**
>
> Any logarithm with a base of e is a natural logarithm.
>
> The abbreviation ln is used for a natural logarithm.

See Chapter 6, Example 33 for finding natural logarithms using a graphing calculator.

> **<u>Change of Base Theorem</u>:**
>
> If x is any positive number and if a and b are positive numbers,
> $a \neq 1, b \neq 1$, then
>
> $$\log_a x = \frac{\log_b x}{\log_b a}$$

Example 5: Find $\log_3 7$ using common logarithms and a calculator.

Solution:

$$\log_3 7 \ = \frac{\log_{10} 7}{\log_{10} 3} \qquad \text{use change of base formula}$$

$$= 1.771243749$$

Example 6: Find $\log_3 7$ using natural logarithms and a calculator.

Solution:

$$\log_3 7 \ = \frac{\log_e 7}{\log_e 3} \ = \ \frac{\ln 7}{\ln 3}$$

$$= \ 1.771243749$$

Graphs of Logarithmic Functions

Example 7.   Find the graph $y = f(x) = \log_6 x$

Solution: Remember that the equation $y = \log_6 x$ is equivalent to the exponential form of this equation: $x = 6^y$.

Make a table by choosing values for y and calculating the x-values.

$x = 6^y$	y	
1	0	$x = 6^y, = 6^0 = 1$
6	1	$x = 6^y, = 6^1 = 6$
36	2	$x = 6^y, = 6^2 = 36$
216	3	$x = 6^y, = 6^3 = 216$
1/6	-1	$x = 6^y, = 6^{-1} = \dfrac{1}{6}$
1/36	-2	$x = 6^y, = 6^{-2} = \dfrac{1}{36}$

Plotting the points we found, the graph is:

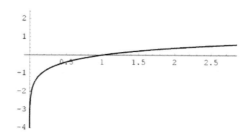

The graph can also be found using a graphing calculator. See Chapter 6, Example 33.

Example 8. Use a table to sketch the graph of $y = f(x) = \ln x$

Solution:

x	$\ln x$
0.5	-0.69314
1	0.0
2	0.69314
3	1.09861
4	1.38629
5	1.60944

The graph found using these points is:

$f(x) = \ln x$

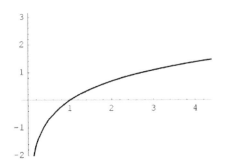

Example 9: Using translations, sketch the graph of $f(x) = \ln(x + 3)$

Solution: We will sketch the graph of $f(x) = \ln x$ shifted left 3 units:

217

Applications

Example 10. The loudness of sounds is measured in units called **decibels.** To measure with this unit, an intensity of I_0 is assigned to a very faint sound, called the **threshold sound**. If a certain sound has intensity I, then the decibel rating of this louder sound is:

$$\text{Decibels} = 10 * \log_{10} \frac{I}{I_0}$$

Find the decibel rating of a sound having an intensity of $100\ I_0$

Solution:

$$\textbf{Decibels} = 10 * \log_{10} \frac{I}{I_0}$$

$$= 10 * \log_{10} \frac{100 I_0}{I_0} \qquad \text{substitute } 100\ I_0 \text{ for } I$$

$$= 10 * \log_{10} 100 \qquad \text{reduce}$$

$$\text{let } \log_{10} 100 = x$$

$$\text{then } 10^x = 100 \qquad \text{use exponential form}$$

$$\text{and } x = 2$$

$$= 10 * x = 10 * 2 = 20 \text{ decibels}$$

Example 11. The intensity of an earthquake, measured on the Richter scale, is

$$\text{Richter} = \log_{10} \frac{I}{I_0} \qquad \text{where } I_0 \text{ is the intensity of an small size earthquake.}$$

Find the Richter scale rating of an earthquake having an intensity of $1{,}000{,}000\ I_0$.

Solution: Richter $= \log_{10} \dfrac{I}{I_0}$

$= \log_{10} \dfrac{1{,}000{,}000 I_0}{I_0}$ substitute $1{,}000{,}000 \ I_0$ for I

$= \log_{10} 1{,}000{,}000$ reduce

let $\log_{10} 1{,}000{,}000 = x$

then $10^x = 1{,}000{,}000$ change to exponential form

and $x = 6$

Richter $= \ 6$

Section 4.3 Exercises

Sketch the graph of each of the following:

1. $x = 3^y$
2. $x = 5^y$
3. $x = (1/4)^y$

4. $x = (3/4)^y$
5. $y = \log_2 x$
6. $y = \log_5 x$

7. $f(x) = \log x$
8. $f(x) = \log_e x$

Find each of the following without the use of a calculator:

9. $\log_2 32$
10. $\log_3 81$
11. $\log_6 36$

12. $\log_7 49$
13. $\log 1$
14. $\log 1000$

15. $\log 0.01$
16. $\log_2 (1/8)$
17. $\ln 0$

18. $\ln 1$
19. $\ln e$
20. $\log 0$

21. $\log 100$
22. $\log 10$
23. $\log_4 4^3$

24. $\log \sqrt{100}$
25. $\log_4 \sqrt[3]{4}$
26. $\log_{25} 5$

27. $\ln e^{1/2}$
28. $\ln \sqrt{e}$

Convert the following to a logarithmic equation:

29. $10^4 = 10,000$
30. $e^4 = z$
31. $m^t = 4$

Convert the following to an exponential equation:

32. $\log_4 4 = 1$
33. $\log 8 = 0.9031$
34. $\ln 15 = 2.7081$

35. $\log_a R = p$
36. $\log_b R^4 = q$

Find the logarithm using common logarithms with the change-of-base formula:

37. $\log_3 24$
38. $\log_7 24$

39. Find the decibel ratings of the following sounds, having intensities as given:

a. whisper, $115\,I_0$

b. truck, $1{,}200{,}000{,}000\,I_0$

c. rock music, $895{,}000{,}000{,}000\,I_0$

d. jet takeoff, $109{,}000{,}000{,}000{,}000\,I_0$

40. Find the Richter scale ratings of earthquakes having the following intensities:

a. $1000\,I_0$

b. $1{,}000{,}000\,I_0$

4.4 Logarithmic Function Properties

Properties of Logarithms

If y and z are any positive real numbers, r is any real number, and a is any positive real number, and $a \neq 1$, then

(1) $\log_a yz = \log_a y + \log_a z$

(2) $\log_a \dfrac{y}{z} = \log_a y - \log_a z$

(3) $\log_a y^r = r * \log_a y$

(4) $\log_a a = 1$

(5) $\log_a 1 = 0$

(6) $\log_a a^y = y$

(7) $a^{\log_a y} = y$

The properties of logarithms for the special cases of base ten (the common logarithm) and base equal to e (natural logarithm) are written as shown below:

Common logarithms	Natural logarithms
(1) $\log(yz) = \log y + \log z$	(1) $\ln (yz) = \ln y + \ln z$
(2) $\log \dfrac{y}{z} = \log y - \log z$	(2) $\ln \dfrac{y}{z} = \ln y - \ln z$
(3) $\log u^c = c \log u$	(3) $\ln u^c = c \ln u$

Example 1. Express each product as a sum of logarithms.

   a. $\log_5(7*3)$ b. $\log_3(5*2)$ c. $\log_9(6*4)$

Solution:

   a. $\log_5(7*3) = \log_5 7 + \log_5 3$

   b. $\log_3(5*2) = \log_3 5 + \log_3 2$

   c. $\log_9(6*4) = \log_9 6 + \log_9 4$

Example 2. Express each quotient as the difference of logarithms.

   a. $\log_5 \dfrac{2}{3}$ b. $\log_6 \dfrac{4}{3}$ c. $\log_9 \dfrac{8}{5}$

Solution:

   a. $\log_5 \dfrac{2}{3} = \log_5 2 - \log_5 3$

   b. $\log_6 \dfrac{4}{3} = \log_6 4 - \log_6 3$

   c. $\log_9 \dfrac{8}{5} = \log_9 8 - \log_9 5$

Example 3. Express each of the following as a product.

   a. $\log_a 7^{-4}$ b. $\log_a \sqrt[3]{5}$ c. $\ln x^5$

Solution:

   a. $\log_a 7^{-4} = -4\log_a 7$

   b. $\log_a \sqrt[3]{5} = \log_a 5^{\frac{1}{3}} = \dfrac{1}{3}\log_a 5$

   c. $\ln x^5 = 5\ln x$

Using the Properties of Logarithms

Example 4. Use the properties of logarithms to rewrite each of the following.

a. $\log_a \dfrac{pq}{r^3}$
b. $\log_a \sqrt[4]{n^3}$
c. $\log_b \sqrt{\dfrac{x^3 y^6}{z^4}}$

Solution:

a. $\log_a \dfrac{pq}{r^3} = \log_a p + \log_a q - \log_a r^3 = \log_a p + \log_a q - 3\log_a r$

b. $\log_a \sqrt[4]{n^3} = \log_a n^{3/4} = \dfrac{3}{4}\log_a n$

c. $\log_b \sqrt{\dfrac{x^3 y^6}{z^4}} = \dfrac{1}{2}\log_b \dfrac{x^3 y^6}{z^4}$

$$= \dfrac{1}{2}\left(\log_b x^3 + \log_b y^6 - \log_b z^4\right)$$

$$= \dfrac{3}{2}\log_b x + \dfrac{6}{2}\log_b y - \dfrac{4}{2}\log_b z$$

$$= \dfrac{3}{2}\log_b x + 3\log_b y - 2\log_b z$$

Example 5. Use the properties of logarithms to rewrite as a single logarithm.

a. $\log_4 (x+3) + \log_4 x - \log_4 3$

b. $4\log_a n - 2\log_a p$

c. $\dfrac{1}{2}\log_7 m + \dfrac{5}{2}\log_7 2n - \log_7 m^2 n$

Solution:

a. $\log_4 (x+3) + \log_4 x - \log_4 3 = \log_4 \dfrac{(x+3)x}{3}$

b. $4\log_a n - 2\log_a p \;=\; \log_a n^4 - \log_a p^2 \;=\; \log_a \dfrac{n^4}{p^2}$

c. $\dfrac{1}{2}\log_7 m + \dfrac{5}{2}\log_7 2n - \log_7 m^2 n$

$$=\; \log_7 m^{1/2} + \log_7 (2n)^{5/2} - \log_7 m^2 n$$

$$=\; \log_7 \dfrac{m^{1/2}(2n)^{5/2}}{m^2 n}$$

$$=\; \log_7 \dfrac{2^{5/2} n^{3/2}}{m^{3/2}} \qquad =\; \log_7 \sqrt{\dfrac{32 n^3}{m^3}}$$

Example 6. Assume that $\log_{10} 2 = 0.3010$ *and* $\log_{10} 3 = 0.4771$ find the following.

a. $\log_{10} 6$ b. $\log_{10} 4$ c. $\log_{10} 9$

d. $\log_{10} \dfrac{1}{2}$ e. $\log_{10} 5$ f. $\log_{10} \dfrac{3}{2}$

Solution:

a. $\log_{10} 6 \;=\; \log(3 * 2) = \log 3 + \log 2 = 0.3010 + 0.4771 = 0.7781$

b. $\log_{10} 4 \;=\; \log 2^2 = 2\log 2 = 2(0.3010) = 0.6020$

c. $\log_{10} 9 \;=\; \log 3^2 = 2\log 3 = 2(0.4771) = 0.9542$

d. $\log_{10} \dfrac{1}{2} \;=\; \log 1 - \log 2 = 0 - 0.3010 = -0.3010$

e. $\log_{10} 5 \;=\; \log \dfrac{10}{2} = \log 10 - \log 2 = 1 - 0.3010 = 0.699$

f. $\log_{10} \dfrac{3}{2} \;=\; \log 3 - \log 2 = 0.4771 - 0.3010 = 0.1761$

Example 7. Simplify each of the following.

       a. $\log_a a^5$ b. $\ln e^t$ c. $\log 10^p$

       d. $10^{\log 4r}$ e. $e^{\ln 6}$

Solution:

       a. $\log_a a^5 = 5$

       b. $\ln e^t = t$

       c. $\log 10^p = p$

       d. $10^{\log 4r} = 4r$

       e. $e^{\ln 6} = 6$

Section 4.4 Exercises

Express each product as a sum of logarithms.

1. $\log_4(17 * 12)$

2. $\log_a(4 * 19)$

3. $\log_m 12T$

4. $\log_r yz$

5. $\ln 3x$

6. $\ln st$

Express each quotient as a difference of logarithms.

7. $\log_a \dfrac{m}{n}$

8. $\ln \dfrac{a}{x}$

Express as a product.

9. $\log_9 x^4$

10. $\log_a y^7$

11. $\log_n T^{-4}$

12. $\ln \sqrt{7}$

Express each as a sum and/or difference of logarithms.

13. $\log_7 5rs^3t^6$

14. $\log_a \dfrac{r^3 t^9}{c^2 d^8}$

15. $\log_b \sqrt{\dfrac{x^8}{y^5 z^3}}$

16. $\ln \sqrt[3]{\dfrac{p^6 q^9}{a^4 c^7}}$

Express as one logarithm and simplify.

17. $\log_b 30 + \log_b 4$

18. $\log 10 + \log 100$

19. $\dfrac{1}{2}\log_b x + 3\log_b w - 5\log_b q$

20. $\ln x^5 - 3\ln \sqrt[3]{x}$

If $\log_b 2 = 0.3010$, $\log_b 5 = 0.6990$ and $\log_b 7 = 0.8451$, find each of the following

21. $\log_b 14$

22. $\log_b 49$

23. $\log_b \dfrac{2}{7}$

24. $\log_b 70$

4.5 Logarithmic and Exponential Equations

Solving Logarithmic Equations

We will look at two types of equations containing logarithmic expressions.

Type 1: This type of logarithmic equation contains **only** logarithmic expressions. To solve this type of equation, we use the fact that a logarithmic function is one-to-one. The result of this is the following:

If $x > 0$, $y > 0$, $a > 0$ and $a \neq 1$, then

$$\text{if } \log_a x = \log_a y \quad \text{then} \quad x = y$$

We will use the following techniques to solve this type of logarithmic equation:

To solve type 1 logarithmic equations:

1. use the properties of logarithms to combine all logs on the left of the equal sign into 1 log expression

2. use the properties of logarithms to combine all logs on the right of the equal sign into 1 log expression

the result will be in this form: $\log_a \{\text{expression 1}\} = \log_a \{\text{expression 2}\}$

3. from the statement above, we can then set

expression 1 = expression 2

4. solve the resulting equation

Example 1:   Solve: $\log_4(2x-3) = \log_4 12 - \log_4 3$

Solution: This is a type 1 logarithmic equation. We will use the steps above.

$$\log_4(2x-3) = \log_4 12 - \log_4 3$$

228

$$\log_4(2x-3) = \log_4 \frac{12}{3}$$ change difference of the logs into a quotient

$$\log_4(2x-3) = \log_4 4$$ simplify

$$2x - 3 = 4$$ set log expressions equal

$$2x = 7$$ solve equation

$$x = 7/2$$

Example 2. Solve: $4\log_2 x = 3\log_2 2$

Solution:

$$4\log_2 x = 3\log_2 2$$

$$\log_2 x^4 = \log_2 2^3$$ use exponent log properties

$$x^4 = 2^3$$ set log expressions equal

$$x = \sqrt[4]{8}$$

Example 3. Solve: $\ln x - \ln(x+1) = 3\ln 4$

Solution:

$$\ln x - \ln(x+1) = 3\ln 4$$

$$\ln \frac{x}{x+1} = \ln 4^3$$ use properties of logs

$$\frac{x}{x+1} = 64$$ set log expressions equal

$$x = 64(x+1)$$ solve the equation

$$x = 64x + 64$$

$$-63x = 64$$

$$x = -64/63 \quad \text{or} \quad \text{No Solution}$$

The answer of $-64/63$ that we found is not a solution because when our answer is substituted into the original equation, the problem is trying to take the log of a negative number and negative numbers do not have real-number logarithmic values.

Example 3 can be solved using a graphing calculator. See Chapter 6, Example 35.

Now, we will look at a second type of logarithmic equation.

Type 2: This type of logarithmic equation contains logarithmic expressions but it also contains terms that are not logarithmic expressions.

<u>**To solve type 2 logarithmic equations:**</u>

    1. use algebra to place all of the logarithmic expressions on one side of the equal sign

    2. use the properties of logs to combine all of the logarithmic expressions into one logarithm

the   3. use algebra to place all of the non-logarithmic expressions on the other side of the

       equal sign

    the result of these steps will be: $\log_a \{\text{expression}\} = \text{number}$

    4. transform the result from the logarithmic form to the exponential form

    5. solve the result

Example 4.   Solve: $\log_2(x+7) + \log_2 x = 3$

Solution: This is a type 2 logarithmic equation because the term on the right side of the equal sign does not include a logarithm. We will use the steps above.

$$\log_2(x+7) + \log_2 x = 3$$

$$\log_2[x(x+7)] = 3 \qquad\qquad \text{use properties to combine logs}$$

$$x(x+7) = 2^3 \qquad\qquad \text{transform to exponential form}$$

$$x^2 + 7x = 8 \qquad \text{distribute}$$

$$x^2 + 7x - 8 = 0 \qquad \text{solve the equation}$$

$$(x + 8)(x - 1) = 0 \qquad \text{factor}$$

$$x = -8, 1$$

We cannot take the logarithm of a negative number, and substitution of $x = -8$ would result in such. The only solution to Example 4 is $x = 1$.

Example 4 can be solved using a graphing calculator. See Chapter 6, Example 36.

Example 5. Solve: $\log_4 x = -1$

Solution: The equation is a type 2 logarithmic equation. Use that method for solving.

$$\log_4 x = -1$$

$$4^{-1} = x \qquad \text{transform to exponential form}$$

$$x = \frac{1}{4}$$

Check: $\log_4 x = -1$

$$\log_4 \frac{1}{4} = -1$$

$$\log_4 4^{-1} = -1$$

$$-1 = -1$$

This problem can be solved using a graphing calculator. See Chapter 6, Example 37.

Example 6. Solve: $\log_3 (x + 3) + \log_3 (x + 5) = 1$

Solution:
$$\log_3 (x + 3) + \log_3 (x + 5) = 1$$

$$\log_3[(x+3)(x+5)] = 1 \qquad \text{use properties}$$

$$(x+3)(x+5) = 3^1 \qquad \text{transform}$$

$$x^2 + 8x + 15 = 3 \qquad \text{F.O.I.L.}$$

$$x^2 + 8x + 12 = 0 \qquad \text{solve}$$

$$(x+6)(x+2) = 0$$

$$x = -6, -2$$

Check: $\log_3(x+3) + \log_3(x+5) = 1$

For $x = -6$

$$\log_3(-6+3) + \log_3(-6+5)$$

this value results in taking the log of negative number which is undefined.

For $x = -2$

$$\log_3(-2+3) + \log_3(-2+5)$$
$$\log_3 1 + \log_3 3$$
$$0 + 1 = 1$$

solution is $x = -2$

Example 6 can be solved using a graphing calculator. See Chapter 6, Example 38

Solving Exponential Equations

Equations are called <u>exponential equations</u> when variables occur in the exponents.

Some equations, such as $3^{2x} = 81$, can be written so that each side has the same base raised to an exponent:

$$3^{2x} = 81$$

$$3^{2x} = 3^4$$

232

Equations with Exponentials of the same base:

if $a > 0$ and $\neq 1$, then

if $a^r = a^s$ then $r = s$

The last rule states that when bases are the same, then the exponents are equal. We can set the exponents equal to each other and solve the resulting equation.

if $\qquad 3^{2x} = 3^4$

then $\qquad 2x = 4 \qquad$ and $\qquad x = 2$

We were able to solve this problem because we could reduce both sides of the equation to the same base.

Example 7. Solve: $2^{4x-11} = 32$

Solution:

$2^{4x-11} = 32$

$2^{4x-11} = 2^5 \qquad\qquad\qquad$ convert both sides to the same base

$4x - 11 = 5 \qquad\qquad\qquad$ set exponents equal

$4x = 16 \qquad\qquad\qquad\qquad$ solve

$x = 4$

Check:

$2^{4x-11} = 32$
$2^{4(4)-11}$
$2^{16-11} \quad = \quad 2^5 \quad = \quad 32$

Example 7 can be solved using a graphing calculator. See Chapter 6, Example 39.

When an exponential equation problem is such that we are **unable** to convert both sides to the same base, we must use another method to solve the problem.

> **To Solve Exponential Equations:**
>
> 1. isolate the exponential term
>
> 2. take the natural or common logarithm of both sides
>
> 3. use exponent operations for logarithms to solve for the variable

Example 8. Solve: $3^x = 22$

Solution:

$$3^x = 22$$

We cannot reduce both sides to the same base, so we will take the logarithm of both sides.

$\log 3^x = \log 22$ take the common log of both sides

$x \log 3 = \log 22$ use exponent property

$x = \dfrac{\log 22}{\log 3}$ this is the exact value of x

Use a calculator with logarithm function to approximate the answer.

$x = 2.8136$

Example 8 can be solved using a graphing calculator. See Chapter 6, Example 40.

Example 9. Solve: $2 = e^{0.4t}$

Solution:

$$2 = e^{0.4t}$$

$\ln 2 = \ln e^{0.4t}$ take the natural log of both sides

$\ln 2 = 0.4t \ln e$ use exponent property

$\ln 2 = 0.4t$ $\ln e = 1$

$$t = \frac{\ln 2}{0.4}$$ this is the exact value of t

Use a calculator to approximate the solution.

$x = 1.7329$

Example 9 can be solved using a graphing calculator. See Chapter 6, Example 41.

Example 10.   Solve $e^x + e^{-x} - 8 = 0$

Solution:

$$e^x + e^{-x} - 8 = 0$$

In this problem there is more than one term with a variable in the exponent. To begin with we will solve this problem for e^x.

$$e^x + \frac{1}{e^x} - 8 = 0$$ change from negative exponent to positive

$$e^{2x} + 1 - 8e^x = 0$$ multiply both sides by e^x to remove fraction

To simplify our equation, let $u = e^x$

$$u^2 - 8u + 1 = 0$$ solve for u

$$u = \frac{-(-8) \pm \sqrt{(-8)^2 - 4(1)(1)}}{2(1)}$$ use quadratic formula

$$u = \frac{8 \pm \sqrt{60}}{2} = \frac{8 \pm 2\sqrt{15}}{2}$$

$$u = 4 \pm \sqrt{15}$$

$$e^x = 4 \pm \sqrt{15}$$ replace u with e^x

We have an exponential equation and will solve by taking the natural log of both sides

$$\ln e^x = \ln(4 \pm \sqrt{15})$$

$$x = \ln(4 \pm \sqrt{15}) \qquad\qquad \ln e^x = x$$

Using a calculator to approximate the solutions, we find:

$$x = 2.0634 \text{ and } -2.0634.$$

Example 10 can be solved using a graphing calculator. See Chapter 6, Example 42.

Section 4.5 Exercises

Solve the following exponential equations.

1. $4^x = 64$

2. $2^{5x} = 16$

3. $3^x = 28$

4. $4^{4x-8} = 128$

5. $81 = 3^{4x} * 9^{2x}$

6. $37^x = 74$

7. $2^{3x-1} = 1/2$

8. $e^r = 10,000$

9. $e^{-0.4t} = 0.06$

10. $3^{2x} = 4^{x-1}$

11. $(5.3)^x = 52$

12. $e^x + e^{-x} = 4$

Solve the logarithmic equations.

13. $\log_4 x = 9$

14. $\log x = -6$

15. $\ln x = 2$

16. $\log_2(8 + 4x) = 6$

17. $\log x + \log(x - 3) = 1$

18. $\log_2(x + 5) - \log_2(x + 1) = \log_2 x$

19. $2\ln(x + 3) - \ln(x + 1) = 3\ln 2$

20. $\log_3(3x) = \log_3 x + \log_3(4 - x)$

21. $\ln(x + 2) = \ln e^{\ln 2} - \ln x$

22. $\log_4(x + 1) = 2 + \log_4(3x - 2)$

23. $\log_8(x - 5) = 2/3$

24. $\log \sqrt{x} = \log(x - 6)$

Section 4.6 Applications

Law of <u>Growth (or Decay)</u> Formula:

Let q_0 be the value of a quantity q at the time $t = 0$ (q_0 is the initial value of q)

If q changes instantaneously at a rate proportional to its current value, then

$$q = q_0 e^{rt}$$

where $r > 0$ is the rate of growth and $r < 0$ is the rate of decay

The next examples show applications of exponential and logarithmic equations.

Example 1. Population Growth:

Suppose the function

$$P(t) = 100,000 e^{.3t}$$

gives the population of a certain city at time t measured in years. In how many years will the population of the city double?

Since the population of the city is 100,000 when $t = 0$, we want to find the value of t for which $P(t) = 200,000$.

Replace $P(t)$ with 200,000 in the original function and we get

$$200,000 = 100,000 \, e^{.3t}$$

or

$$2 = e^{.3t}$$

To solve for t, take the natural logarithms of both sides of the equation.

$$\ln 2 = \ln e^{.3t}$$

$$\ln 2 = 0.3t \ln e \qquad \text{use properties}$$

$$\ln 2 = 0.3t \qquad \ln e = 1$$

238

and

$$t = \frac{\ln 2}{0.3} \qquad \text{this is the exact value answer}$$

Using a calculator with a logarithm function, $t = 2.3105$ years.

Example 2: Half-life of a Radioactive Substance

Suppose the amount, $I(t)$, in grams of a certain radioactive substance at a time t is given by

$$I(t) = I_0 e^{-.2t}$$

where I_0 is the amount of the substance initially (when $t = 0$) and t is measured in days.

Find the *half-life* of the substance, that is, the time it takes for half of a given amount of the substance to decay.

We want to find the time t that must elapse for $I(t)$ to be reduced to a value equal to $I_0/2$.

That is we want to solve the equation

$$(1/2)\, I_0 = I_0 e^{-.2t}$$

Dividing both sides by I_0, we get

$$1/2 = e^{-.2t}$$

Take the natural logarithm of both sides,

$$\ln 1/2 = \ln e^{-.2t}$$

Using the properties of logarithms

$$\ln 1/2 = -0.2t \ln e$$

Remember that $\ln e = 1$

$$\ln 1/2 = -0.2t$$

$$t = \frac{-\ln 1/2}{0.2}$$ answer is the exact value

Using a calculator with a natural logarithm key, we find

$$t = 3.4657 \quad \text{or} \quad \text{approximately } 3.466 \text{ days}$$

Example 3.   Carbon 14 Dating

Carbon 14 is a radioactive isotope of carbon which has a half-life of about 5600 years. The earth's atmosphere contains much carbon, mostly in the form of carbon dioxide, with small traces of carbon 14. Most of this atmospheric carbon is in the form of the non-radioactive isotope carbon 12. The ratio of carbon 14 to carbon 12 is virtually constant in the atmosphere.

However, as a plant absorbs carbon dioxide from the air in the process of photosynthesis, the carbon 12 stays in the plant while the carbon 14 decays by conversion to nitrogen. Thus, the ratio of carbon 14 to carbon 12 is smaller in the plant than it is in the atmosphere. Even when the plant is eaten by an animal, this ratio will continue to decrease. Based on these facts, a method of dating objects called *carbon 14 dating* has been developed.

Let R be the (nearly constant) ratio of carbon 14 to carbon 12 found in the atmosphere. Let r be the ratio found in a fossil.

It can be shown that the relationship between R and r is given by

$$\frac{R}{r} = e^{(t \ln 2)/5600}$$

where t is the age of the fossil in years.

If we verify the formula for $t = 0$, we get:

$$\frac{R}{r} = e^0 = 1$$

Since the ratio equals 1, it follows that $R = r$, so that the ratio in the fossil is the same as the ratio in the atmosphere. This is true only when $t = 0$.

Let's verify the formula for $t = 5600$.

$$\frac{R}{r} = e^{(5600 \ln 2)/5600}$$

$$\frac{R}{r} = e^{\ln 2} = 2 \qquad \text{and} \qquad r = 1/2R$$

From this last result, we see that the ratio in the fossil is half the ratio in the atmosphere. Since the half-life of carbon 14 is 5600 years, we expect only half of it to remain at the end of that time. Thus, the formula gives the correct result for $t = 5600$.

Example 4   Continuously Compounded Interest

The formula for calculating continuously compounded interest is given by

$$A = Pe^{rt}$$

where P is the principal, r is the annual interest rate expressed as a decimal, t is the number of years of investment, and A is the amount after t years.

Suppose \$30,000 is deposited in a money market account that pays interest at the rate of 5% per year compounded continuously.

Find the balance in the account after 6 years

$$A = Pe^{rt}$$

Substitute in values

$$A = 30,000 \, e^{0.05(6)} \;=\; 30,000 \, e^{0.3} \qquad \text{this is the exact value}$$

Using a calculator with logarithm functions to find the approximate value for A, we find

$$A = \$40,495.76$$

Suppose $10,000 is invested at an interest rate of r, compounded continuously, and grows to an amount of $14,190.68 in 5 years.

Find the interest rate at which the original $10,000 was invested.

$$A = Pe^{rt}$$

$$14,190.68 = 10,000\, e^{5r}$$

$$\frac{14190.68}{10,000} = e^{5r}$$

$$1.419068 = e^{5r}$$

$$\ln 1.419068 = \ln e^{5r}$$

$$\ln 1.419068 = 5r$$

$$r = \frac{\ln 1.419068}{5} \qquad \text{this is the exact value.}$$

Use a calculator to approximate the value of r.

$$r = 0.07000 = 7\%$$

The last example can be solved using a graphing calculator. See Chapter 6 , Example 43.

Section 4.6 Exercises

1. The 1980 population of the United States was approximately 231 million, and the population has been growing continuously at a rate of 1.03% per year. Predict the population in the year 2025 if the growth trend continues.

2. The 1985 population estimate for India was 766 million, and the population has been growing continuously at a rate of about 1.8% per year. Assuming that this rapid growth rate continues, estimate the population of India in the year 2025.

3. In fishery science, the collection of fish that results from one annual reproduction is called a cohort. It is usually assumed that the number of fish $N(t)$ still alive after t years is given by an exponential function. For one type of fish, $N(t) = N_0 e^{-0.15t}$, where N_0 is the initial size of the cohort. If the cohort for a specific year is 25 million, how many of that cohort will be alive after 10 years?

4. The amount of a radioactive substance present at time t measured in seconds is $A(t) = 4000e^{-5t}$. Find the half-life of the substance, that is, the time it when only half of the substance remains.

5. Find the half-life of a radioactive specimen if the amount y in grams present at time t in days is $y = 2000e^{-5t}$

6. The number of rabbits in a colony is $y = y_0 e^{5t}$ where t represents time in months and y_0 is the rabbit population when $t = 0$. If $y_0 = 200$, find the rabbits present at time $t = 5$.

7. Refer to problem 6 above. How long will it take for the rabbits to quadruple?

8. Suppose an Egyptian mummy is discovered in which the ratio of carbon 14 to carbon 12 is about one-fourth the ratio found in the atmosphere. About how long ago did the Egyptian die? Refer to Example 3 in this section.

9. If the ratio of carbon 14 to carbon 12 in an object is 1/5 the atmospheric ratio, how old is the object? Refer to Example 3 in this section.

10. Using the formula given in Example 3, if an object is found that contains 20% of the normal amount of carbon 14, how old is the object?

11. Using the formula given in Example 3, solve the formula for t.

12. If $20,000 is deposited into an account that is compounded continuously at an interest rate of 5%, what amount of money will be in the account after 10 years?

13. If 40,000 is invested in an account that pays interest compounded continuously at 4% interest, how long will it take to double the initial investment?

14. Using the formula for compounded continuously interest: $A = Pe^{rt}$, solve for r.

15. Using the formula for compounded continuously interest: $A = Pe^{rt}$, solve for t.

Chapter 4 Summary

To find Inverse Relations:
    1. **Given Ordered Pairs: interchange coordinates**
    2. **Given Equation: interchange the variables**
    3. **Given Graph: Reflect across the line $y = x$**

One-to-One Functions:
    Prove: If $f(a) = f(b)$, then show $a = b$
    Show: Horizontal Line test

Inverse of a Function:
    1. **Replace $f(x)$ with y**
    2. **Interchange x and y**
    3. **Solve for y**
    4. **Replace y with f^{-1}**

Composition of a Function and its Inverse:
$$(f^{-1} \circ f)(x) = f^{-1}(f(x)) = x \quad \text{for any } x \text{ in the domain of } f$$
$$(f \circ f^{-1})(x) = f(f^{-1}(x)) = x \quad \text{for any x in the domain of } f^{-1}$$

Exponential function:
$$f(x) = a^x, \quad a > 0 \quad \text{and} \quad a \neq 1,$$

Interest: **Compound:** $A = P\left(1 + \dfrac{r}{n}\right)^{nt}$

            Compound Continuously: $A = Pe^{rt}$

Euler's number e: = 2.718281828

Logarithm/Exponential Form: $y = \log_a x$ **if and only if**
$x = a^y$

<u>Change of Base Theorem</u>: $\log_a x = \dfrac{\log_b x}{\log_b a}$

Properties of Logarithms

(1) $\log_a yz = \log_a y + \log_a z$

(2) $\log_a \dfrac{y}{z} = \log_a y - \log_a z$

(3) $\log_a y^r = r * \log_a y$

(4) $\log_a a = 1$

(5) $\log_a 1 = 0$

(6) $\log_a a^y = y$

(7) $a^{\log_a y} = y$

To solve logarithmic equations:

   When: $\log_a \{\text{expression 1}\} = \log_a \{\text{expression 2}\}$

   expression 1 = expression 2

   When: $\log_a \{\text{expression}\} = \text{number}$

   transform the result from the logarithmic form to the exponential form

To solve exponential equations:

   1. When: $a^r = a^s$ then $r = s$
   2. Isolate the exponential term and
      take the natural or common logarithm of both sides

Chapter 4 Review

Find the inverse of the relation:
1. $\{(1, -2), (4, 1), (7, 4), (10, 7)\}$

Find an equation of the inverse relation:
2. $y = -3x + 4$

3. $y = 2x^2 + 3x + 1$

Which of the following is one-to-one:
4. $f(x) = 4x - 2$

5. $f(x) = 4x^2 - 2x$

6. $f(x) = 4x^3 - 2$

Find the inverse of the following:
7. $f(x) = 4 - 3x$

8. $f(x) = \sqrt[3]{x - 2}$

9. $f(x) = e^x$

10. $f(x) = \log x$

Match the equations listed with one of the graphs below:
11. $f(x) = \log_2 x$

12. $f(x) = \log_3(x + 2)$

13. $f(x) = (2/3)^x$

14. $f(x) = 4^x + 2$ 15. $f(x) = e^x - 3$

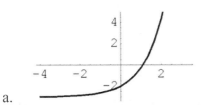

a.

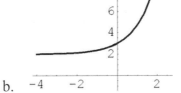

b.

c.

d.

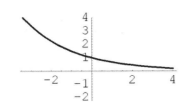

e.

Find the value of each of the following without a calculator
16. $\log_8 64$

17. $\log 1{,}000$

18. $\ln e^2$

19. $\log 10^3$

247

Convert to an exponential equation:

20. $\log_3 x = 2$

21. $\log_b M = N$

Convert to a logarithmic equation:

22. $5^{-2} = 1/25$

23. $e^x = 40$

Use the change of base formula to find the logarithm

24. $\log_4 10$

Express in terms of sums and differences of logarithms:

25. $\log \dfrac{x^2 y^4}{z^5}$

Solve:

26. $\log_3 x = 4$

27. $4^{x-1} = 8^x$

28. $\log_x 32 = 5$

29. $\log_2 x + \log_2 (x - 6) = 4$

30. $\log x^2 - \log x = 0$

CHAPTER 5

SYSTEMS OF EQUATIONS AND INEQUALITIES

Section 5.1 Linear Systems of Equations with Two Variables

System of Equations:

      Any set of equations is a system of equations.

      The solution set of a system is the intersection of the solution sets of the individual equations.

      Example of a system of equations:

$$2x + y = 8$$
$$x - y = 1$$

Linear Equations are first degree equations. That is, there are no variables raised to an exponent higher than one.

Remember that the solution set of a linear equation in two variables is an infinite set of ordered pairs which are the points on the graph. The graph of a linear equation is a straight line. There are three possibilities for the solution set of a system of two linear equations in two variables.

a. $2x - y = 4$
     $x + y = 5$

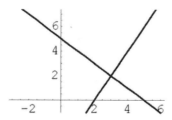

The solution to the system is the intersection of the two lines.

The solution is the point (3, 2).

b. $3x + 2y = -4$
   $3x + 2y = 3$

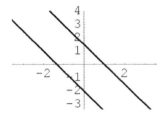

These two lines are parallel and do not intersect.
There is no solution.

c. $x + y = 5$
   $2y = -2x + 10$

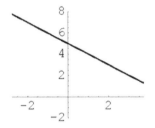

These two lines are actually the same line.
The solution set is all of the points on the line.

Graphs of Linear Systems with two equations and two variables

1. The two graphs intersect in a single point. The coordinates of this point are the solution of the system.

2. The graphs are distinct parallel lines. When this happens, the system is **inconsistent.** The lines do not intersect and have no common points. There is no solution.

3. The graphs are the same line. In this situation, the equations are **dependent**. There are infinite solutions to this system. These are the points on the line.

Solving a system of linear equations with two variables.

Methods used to solve a system of linear equations with two variables:

1. Graph both equations and find the point of intersection.

2. Use the Substitution Method.

3. Use the Addition Method.

Graphing Method:

1. Graph each line.
2. Find the point of intersection which is the solution to the system.

When we graph a system of equations, we can usually see the approximate solution of a linear system.

It is difficult to determine the exact values of the solution of the system by looking at the graph unless a graphing calculator is used.

Substitution Method:

1. Solve one of the equations for one of the variables.
2. Substitute this solution into the other equation and thus get an equation in only one variable.
3. Find the solution to this new equation found in step 2.
4. Substitute the solution found in step 3 back into one of the original equations to find the value of the other variable.
5. Check the solution in both of the given equations.

Example 1. Use the substitution method to solve the given system.

$$x + y = 2$$
$$x + 3y = -2$$

Solution:

Solve the first equation for x.

$$x = 2 - y$$

Substitute this solution into the second equation in place of x.

$$(2 - y) + 3y = -2$$

$$2 - y + 3y = -2 \qquad \text{remove parenthesis}$$

$$2 + 2y = -2 \qquad \text{collect like terms}$$

$$2y = -4 \qquad \text{subtract 2 from both sides}$$

$$y = -2 \qquad \text{divide}$$

Substitute -2 back into the first equation in place of y and solve for x.

$$x - 2 = 2 \qquad \text{or} \quad x = 4$$

The solution to the given system is the point of intersection $(4, -2)$

Addition (sometimes called "Elimination") Method:

1. Multiply the two equations by suitable numbers, so that when the equations are added, one of the variables is eliminated.
2. Add the two new equations.
3. The result is a new equation in only one variable.
4. Solve this single variable equation.
5. Substitute the solution back into one of the original equations to obtain the value of the second variable.
6. Check the solution in both of the given equations.

Example 2: Use the addition method to solve the given system.

$$3x + 4y = 5$$
$$2x + 3y = 4$$

Solution: Multiply the first equation by -2 and the second equation by 3 to eliminate x when the equations are added.

$$-6x - 8y = -10$$
$$6x + 9y = 12$$

Add the two new equations.

$$y = 2$$

Substitute this value into the first equation in place of y.

$$3x + 4(2) = 5$$

Solve for the other variable x.

$$3x + 8 = 5$$

$$3x = -3$$

$$x = -1$$

The solution is $(-1,\ 2)$

Example 2 can be solved using a graphing calculator as shown in Chapter 6, Example 44.

Example 3. Solve the system using the addition method.

$$-3x + 2y = 4$$
$$6x - 4y = 7$$

Solution: We will eliminate the x variable by multiplying the first equation by 2.

$$-6x + 4y = 8$$
$$6x - 4y = 7$$

Adding the two equations, we get

$$0 = 15$$

Both variables are eliminated and the result is the <u>false</u> statement $0 = 15$. Because this is a false statement, there is no solution to this system, and we know that the lines are parallel.

Example 4. Solve the system using the addition method.

$$4x - y = -2$$
$$-4x + y = 2$$

Solution: We do not need to multiply either equation because we can see that if we add The equations we will eliminate x.

Adding the two equations, we get

$$0 = 0$$

Both variables were eliminated and the result is a <u>true</u> statement $0 = 0$. The true statement tells us that the solution is an infinite number of points. (The graph of the equations are the same line.)

Applications

Example 5. The owner of a golf shop ordered 10 putters and 12 drivers for $1150. In a second purchase he ordered 4 putters and 3 drivers for $325. Find the cost of each of the golf clubs.

Solution: We will write a system of equations to solve this problem.

Let

x = the cost of the putter

y = the cost of the driver

Using the data from the first purchase we have the equation

$$10x + 12y = 1150$$

From the data of the second purchase we have the equation

$$4x + 3y = 325$$

The two equations are a system which we will solve.

$$10x + 12y = 1150$$
$$4x + 3y = 325$$

Looking at the system we see that if we multiply the second equation by -4, we will eliminate the y variable when we add the two equations.

$$10x + 12y = 1150$$
$$-16x - 12y = -1300$$

Add the two equations.

$$-6x = -150$$

Solve this equation.

$$x = 25$$

Substitute 25 for x into the first equation we.

$$10(25) + 12y = 1150$$

Solve this equation to find the value of y.

$$250 + 12y = 1150$$

$$12y = 900 \qquad \text{then} \qquad y = 75$$

Thus, the cost of each putter is $25 and the cost of each driver is $75

Example 6. John wants to invest $30,000. With part of his money he buys shares in a mutual fund, paying interest of 9% per year. He invests the rest of his money in municipal bonds paying interest of10% per year. After one year John earns interest of $2820. How much is invested at each rate?

Solution: We will write a system of equations to solve this problem.

Let

$x =$ the amount of money invested at 9%

$y =$ the amount of money invested at 10%

Write the first equation about the total money invested.

$$x + y = 30000$$

The second equation will calculate the interest earned in 1 year.

$$0.09x + 0.10y = 2820$$

The system is
$$x + y = 30000$$
$$0.09x + 0.10y = 2820$$

Looking at our equations, we will multiply the first equation by -9 and the second equation by 100.

$$-9x - 9y = -270000$$

$$9x + 10y = 282000$$

Adding and eliminating x, we find the value of y.

$$y = 12000$$

257

Substituting into the first equation, we find x.

$$x + 12000 = 30000$$

$$x = 18000$$

John invested $18,000 at 9% and $12,000 at 10%.

Example 6 can be solved using a graphing calculator. See Chapter 6, Example 45.

Example 7. Six hundred tickets were sold for a school play. The price of an adult ticket was $3.00 and a child's ticket was $1.00. If the ticket sales produced a total of $1400, how many tickets of each kind were sold?

Solution: Write a system of equations to solve this problem.

Let
x = the number of adult tickets sold

y = the number of child tickets sold

Write the first equation about the total number of the tickets.

$$x + y = 600$$

The second equation will be about the money.

$$3.00x + 1.00y = 1400$$

The system is:

$$x + y = 600$$
$$3x + 1y = 1400$$

To solve the system of equations use the addition method.

Multiply the first equation by -3.

$$-3x - 3y = -1800$$
$$3x + y = 1400$$

Add the equations and eliminate x.

$$-2y = -400 \qquad \text{then} \qquad y = 200$$

Substitute this value of y into the first equation to find x.

$$x + 200 = 600$$

$$x = 400$$

The solution shows that 400 adult tickets and 200 child tickets were sold.

This example can be solved using a graphing calculator. See Chapter 6, Example 46.

Section 5.1 Exercises

Solve graphically.

1.
$$x + y = 3$$
$$2x + y = 5$$

2.
$$x + y = 1$$
$$3x - y = 3$$

3.
$$x + 2y = 6$$
$$3x + y = 3$$

4.
$$x - 2y = 0$$
$$2x - 3y = 2$$

5.
$$x + y = 0$$
$$2x - 2y = -4$$

6.
$$2x - 3y = 3$$
$$3x + y = 10$$

Solve using the substitution method.

7.
$$x + y = 5$$
$$2x - y = 4$$

8.
$$2x - 3y = 1$$
$$4x + y = -5$$

9.
$$y + 2x = 6$$
$$4x - y = 6$$

10.
$$2x + 4y = 6$$
$$3x - y = 2$$

11.
$$2x - 4y = -4$$
$$3x + 2y = 10$$

12.
$$3x - 3y = 3$$
$$4x + 4y = 12$$

Solve using the addition method.

13.
$$x + 3y = 5$$
$$x - 3y = -1$$

14.
$$x + 2y = 8$$
$$x + 2y = 4$$

15.
$$3x + 4y = 6$$
$$4x - 3y = 8$$

16.
$$2x + y = 7$$
$$3x - 2y = 7$$

17.
$$2x - 3y = 10$$
$$-4x + 6y = 15$$

18.
$$6x - 4y = 14$$
$$4x + 3y = 11$$

19.
$$0.5x - 0.4y = 1$$
$$0.3x + 0.2y = 0.6$$

20.   On July 4th Six Flags Amusement Park sold 35,000 tickets and collected $1,375,000 in ticket sales. If adult tickets were sold that day for $50 and child tickets were sold for $35, how many tickets of each kind were sold?

21.   On October 12th Six Flags Amusement Park sold 15,000 tickets and collected $510,000 in ticket sales. If adult tickets were sold that day for $40 and child tickets were sold for $30, how many tickets of each kind were sold?

22.   How much lowfat milk that is 3% butterfat should be mixed with milk that is 14% butterfat to get 25 gallons of lowfat milk that is 8.72% butterfat?

23.   How much saline solution that is 20% saline must be added to a second solution that is 2% saline to produce twenty-five gallons of a mixture that is 5.6% saline?

24.   If Paul has $20,000 to invest, he will split the total amount between two funds. One fund will pay 7% and the other pays 4%. How much will he invest in each to have a profit of $1250?

Section 5.2 Linear Systems with Three Variables

A solution of a linear equation of the form

$$Ax + By + Cz = K \qquad \text{(an equation with three variables)}$$

is an **ordered triple (x, y, z).**

An example would be:

triplet $(1, \ 2, \ 4)$ is a solution of the equation $2x + 3y - z = 4$

The solution set of such an equation is an infinite number of ordered triples.

Solving a System with Three Variables

To solve a system with three or more variables use the addition method repeatedly:

To Solve a System with Three Variables:
1. Eliminate the same variable from each of two pairs of equations.
2. Then using the resulting equations, eliminate another variable.
3. The result of step 2 will be an equation containing only one variable.
4. Solve this equation for the value of the variable.
5. Substitute this value into one of the resulting equations found in step 1.
6. Solve for the second variable.
7. Substitute both of the values of the variables back into one of the original equations to find the value of the third variable.
8. İt is helpful to number the equations as you go.

Example 1. Solve the system:

$$
\begin{array}{ll}
2x + y - z = 2 & (1) \\
x + 3y + 2z = 1 & (2) \\
x + y + z = 2 & (3)
\end{array}
$$

Solution:

We will choose to eliminate x first from equations (1) and (2). Multiply both sides of equation (2) by -2.

Add equations (1) and (2).

$$2x + y - z = 2 \qquad \text{(1)}$$
$$-2x - 6y - 4x = -2 \qquad \text{(2) multiplied by } -2$$
$$\overline{}$$
$$-5y - 5z = 0 \qquad \text{call this new equation (4)}$$

The variable x must be eliminated again from a different pair of equations. Let's use (2) and (3). Multiply both sides of equation (2) by -1 and add the result to equation (3).

$$-x - 3y - 2z = -1 \qquad \text{(2) multiplied by } -1$$
$$x + y + z = 2 \qquad \text{(3)}$$
$$\overline{}$$
$$-2y - z = 1 \qquad \text{call this new equation (5)}$$

Now solve the system formed by the two new equations (4) and (5). To eliminate z, multiply both sides of equation (4) by -1 and both sides of equation (5) by 5 and add these equations.

$$5y + 5z = 0 \qquad \text{(4) multiplied by } -1$$
$$-10y - 5z = 5 \qquad \text{(5) multiplied by 5}$$
$$\overline{}$$
$$-5y = 5 \qquad \text{or} \qquad y = -1$$

Substitute -1 into equation (5) for y.

$$-2(-1) - z = 1$$

Solve for z: $\quad 2 - z = 1 \quad \rightarrow \quad -z = -1 \quad \rightarrow \quad z = 1$

To find x, substitute the values we found for the variables y and z into equation (3).

$$x + y + z = 2 \qquad\qquad \text{equation (3)}$$

$$x - 1 + 1 = 2 \qquad \text{or} \qquad x = 2$$

Thus the ordered triple which is the solution of the system is $(2, -1, 1)$

Example 2. Solve the system:

$$x - y + z = 0 \qquad\qquad (1)$$
$$x - 2y + 3z = -5 \qquad\qquad (2)$$
$$2x + 3y - z = 11 \qquad\qquad (3)$$

Solution:

Let's choose to eliminate z first. Multiply both sides of equation (1) by -3. Then add equations (1) and (2):

$$-3x + 3y - 3z = 0 \qquad\qquad \text{(1) multiplied by } -3.$$
$$x - 2y + 3z = -5 \qquad\qquad \text{(2)}$$

$$-2x + y = -5 \qquad\qquad \text{call this equation (4)}$$

The variable z must be eliminated again from a different pair of equations. Let's use (2) and (3). Multiply both sides of equation (3) by 3 and add the result to equation (2).

$$6x + 9y - 3z = 33 \qquad\qquad \text{(3) multiplied by 3}$$
$$x - 2y + 3z = -5 \qquad\qquad \text{(2)}$$

$$7x + 7y = 28 \qquad\qquad \text{divide the new equation}$$
$$\text{by 7}$$

$$x + y = 4 \qquad\qquad \text{call this equation (5)}$$

Solve the system formed by the two new equations (4) and (5). To eliminate y, multiply both sides of equation (5) by -1 and add these equations.

$$-x - y = -4 \qquad\qquad \text{(5) multiplied by } -1$$
$$-2x + y = -5$$

$$\overline{}$$

$$-3x = -9 \qquad \text{or} \qquad x = 3$$

Substitute 3 into equation (5) for x.

$$3 + y = 4 \qquad \text{or} \qquad y = 1$$

Use equation (1) to find z by substituting the x and y values for the variables x and y.

$$x - y + z = 0 \qquad\qquad\qquad (1)$$

$$3 - 1 + z = 0 \qquad \text{or} \qquad z = -2$$

Thus the ordered triple which is the solution of the system is (3, 1, − 2).

Applications:

We encounter systems of equations with three or more variables in many areas. In fields of science and business/finance systems of equations are often used to solve problems.

Example 3. An organic farm is going to plant three crops on ten acres of land. Potatoes, corn and beans will be planted. The area acreage needed for corn is twice as much as the acreage needed for potatoes, and the beans crop will use two acres less than the acreage needed for the potatoes. Find the acreage used for each crop.

Solution:

Let x represent the acres used for the corn crop.
Let y represent the acres used for the bean crop.
Let z represent the acres used for the potato crop.

Since the total acreage used is 10, we have:

$$x + y + z = 10 \qquad\qquad (1)$$

Using the statement from the problem:
acreage needed for corn is twice as much as for potatoes, we get:

$$x = 2z \qquad \text{or}$$

$$x - 2z = 0 \qquad\qquad (2)$$

Using the statement from the problem:
bean crop will use two acres less than the potatoes, we get:

$$y = z - 2 \qquad \text{or}$$

$$y - z = -2 \qquad\qquad (3)$$

We now have a system of three equations:

$$
\begin{array}{ll}
x + y + z = 10 & (1) \\
x - 2z = 0 & (2) \\
y - z = -2 & (3)
\end{array}
$$

Use equations (1) and (2) to eliminate x. Multiply (2) by -1 and add to (1).

$$
\begin{array}{ll}
x + y + z = 10 & (1) \\
-x \quad + 2z = 0 & (2) \text{ times } -1 \\
\hline
\quad y + 3z = 10 & (4)
\end{array}
$$

Use (3) and (4) to eliminate z Multiply (3) by -1 and add.

$$
\begin{array}{ll}
-y + z = 2 & (3) \text{ times } -1 \\
y + 3z = 10 & (4) \\
\hline
\quad 4z = 12 \qquad \text{or} \qquad z = 3 &
\end{array}
$$

Substitute the value for z into equation (3) to find y.

$$y - 3 = -2 \qquad \text{or} \qquad y = 1$$

Use equation (1) to find x by substituting the values for the variables y and z.

$$x + 1 + 3 = 10 \qquad \text{or} \qquad x = 6$$

The solution is: 6 acres for corn, 1 acre for beans, and 3 acres for potatoes.

Example 4. Anne has $25,000 to invest. She puts part of the money into an account paying 3% interest, part into a second account paying 4% interest, and the rest into an account paying 5% interest. After 1 year the total interest from her three accounts is $1060. She invested $1,000 more into the account paying 4% than in the account paying 3%. Find the amount of money invested in each account.

Solution:

Let x represent the amount invested in the 3% account.
Let y represent the amount invested in the 4% account.
Let z represent the amount invested in the 5% account.

Since the total money invested is 25,000, we have the first equation.

$$x + y + z = 25000 \qquad (1)$$

Since the total interest received is 1060, we have a second equation.

$$0.03x + 0.04y + 0.05z = 1060$$
$$\text{or}$$
$$3x + 4y + 5z = 106000 \qquad (2)$$

From the fact: she invested $1,000 more into the account paying 4% than in the account paying 3%, we have a third equation.

$$x + 1000 = y$$
$$\text{or}$$
$$x - y = -1000 \qquad (3)$$

We now have a system of three equations

$$x + y + z = 25000 \qquad (1)$$
$$3x + 4y + 5z = 106000 \qquad (2)$$
$$x - y = -1000 \qquad (3)$$

Use (1) and (2) to eliminate z. Multiply (1) by -5 and add to (1).

$$-5x - 5y - 5z = -125000 \qquad \text{(1) times } -5$$
$$3x + 4y + 5z = 106000 \qquad \text{(2)}$$

$$-2x - y = -19000$$

or

$$2x + y = 19000 \qquad \text{(4)}$$

Add (3) and (4) to eliminate y.

$$x - y = -1000 \qquad \text{(3)}$$
$$2x + y = 19000 \qquad \text{(4)}$$

$$3x = 18000 \qquad \text{or} \qquad x = 6,000$$

Substitute the value of 6000 for x into equation (3).

$$6000 - y = -1000 \qquad \text{or} \qquad y = 7,000$$

Substitute values for x and y into equation (1).

$$6000 + 7000 + z = 25000 \qquad \text{or} \qquad z = 12,000$$

Anne invested $6,000 at 3%; $7,000 at 4%; and $12,000 at 5%.

Section 5.2 Exercises

Solve each of the following using systems of equations.

1. $x + 2y - 3z = 1$
    $2x - y - z = -3$
    $3x + 3y + 2z = 16$

2. $3x + 4y - z = 7$
    $-2x + 5y + 4z = 2$
    $4x - 7y - 4z = 4$

3. $3x + y - z = 2$
    $-2x - 2y + 3z = -11$
    $x + 3y - 2z = 11$

4. $x + 2y - 3z = 2$
    $2x + 4y = -8$
    $2x + 2z = 4$

5. $2x - y + 2z = 7$
    $x + 2y - z = -9$
    $3x - 4y + 2z = 8$

6. $x + 2y - 3z = -8$
    $3x - y - 2z = 4$
    $4x - 2y - 5z = 5$

7. $3x + 5y + 4z = 1$
    $x + 4y - z = 5$
    $2x - 3y + 4z = -2$

8. $2x + y + z = 1$
    $4x - 2y + 2z = -6$
    $-6x + 3y + 3z = -3$

9. $2x + 2y + 3z = 3$
    $x + 3y + z = 0$
    $4x + 6y - 4z = -5$

10. $2x + y - 3z = 5$
    $x - 2y + 4z = 15$
    $3x + 4y + 2z = -5$

11. $x + 2y + 3z = 5$
    $2x + z = 3$
    $3y - 2z = 11$

12. $x - 2y + 3z = 6$
    $3x - y + 2z = 2$
    $2x - 3y - z = 7$

13. $2x + 4y - z = 3$
    $3x - 5y = -19$
    $4y - 10z = 18$

14. $x + 2y - z = 8$
    $2x - 6y + 2z = -1$
    $3x + 8y + 5z = 1$

15. If Todd had $50,000 to invest. He invested part of his money in bonds paying 4% interest, part in stocks paying 5% interest, and the rest of the money in a hedge fund with interest of 7%. His interest after one year was $2220. If he invested twice as much in bonds as he did in stocks, how much was invested in each type of investment?

16. The choir recently gave a performance for the community. Adult tickets sold for $3, senior tickets for $2 and child tickets for $1. A total of 825 tickets were sold for $1525. If the total of the adult and senior tickets sold were 400 tickets, how many of each were sold?

Section 5.3 Systems of Inequalities

Many mathematical descriptions of real situations are best expressed as inequalities rather than equalities. Quite often a system of inequalities is needed. Perhaps the simplest way to see the solution of an inequality in two variables is to draw a graph.

Linear Inequality in Two Variables:

A linear inequality in 2 variables is an inequality of the form:

$$Ax + By \leq C$$

where A, B, and C are real numbers with A and B not both equal to zero.

The symbols of inequalities can be: $\leq$, $<$, $\geq$, and $>$.

One solution of an inequality in two variables is an ordered pair (x, y).

The solution set of an inequality is the set of all ordered pairs that make the inequality a true statement.

The graph of an inequality is the simplest way to see the solution.

Examples of inequalities in two variables are:

$$3x - 4y < 18$$

$$2x + 36 \leq 12$$

$$x + 7y > 15$$

$$1/2x - 2/3y \geq 6$$

The graph of a linear inequality turns out to be made up of a half-plane with its boundary, the line, perhaps included.

Steps for graphing an inequality with two variables:

1. Graph the line that would result if the inequality sign were changed to an = sign.

2. The line will divide the graph into 2 half-planes. One of these is the solution set.

3. To determine which half-plane (the one above or below the line) is the solution, pick a test point and see if it satisfies the inequality given.

4. If the test point satisfies the given inequality, shade the half-plane that includes the chosen point.

5. If the test point does not satisfy the given inequality, shade the other side of the line.

6. Make the line a solid line if the inequality symbol is either $\geq$ or $\leq$.

7. Make the line a dotted line if the inequality symbol is either $>$ or $<$.

Example 1. Graph $y < x + 4$.

Solution: Follow the steps above. First graph the line $y = x + 4$. Make a table to help you graph the line. The line should be dotted.

Pick a test point. Let's use the point (0, 0). Does it satisfy the inequality?
$$(0) < (0) + 4 \quad \text{or} \quad 0 < 4$$
Since the point **does** satisfy the given inequality, shade the side of the line that **contains** our point.

The shaded area is the solution set to the inequality.

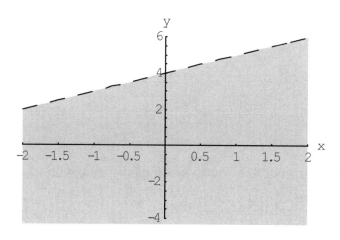

Example 2. Graph: $2x + y \le 6$

Solution: First graph the line : $2x + y = 6$. Make a table to graph the line.

Pick a test point. Let's use the point (0, 0). Does it satisfy the inequality?

$$2(0) + (0) \le 6 \quad \text{or} \quad 0 \le 6$$

Since it **does** satisfy the given inequality, shade the side of the line that **does** contain our point.

The line should be solid since the inequality does contain the equal sign.

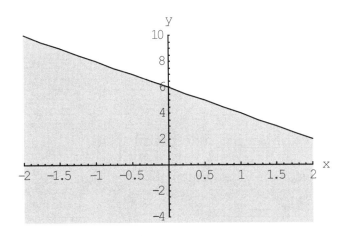

Example 2 can be solved using a graphing calculator. See Chapter 6, Example 47.

Example 3. Graph $x > 2$ on a plane

Solution: First graph the line: $x = 2$. Make a table to graph the line.

The line should be dotted since the inequality does not contain the equal sign.

Pick a test point. Let's use the point (0, 0). Does it satisfy the inequality?

$$(0) > 2 \quad \text{or} \quad 0 > 2$$

Since it **does not** satisfy the given inequality, shade the side of the line that **does not** contain our point.

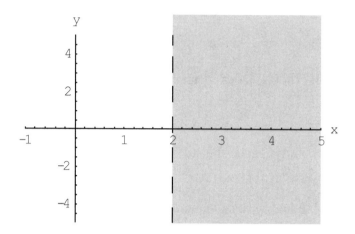

Example 4: Graph $y \leq 5$ on a plane.

Solution: First graph the line: $y = 5$. Make a chart to graph the line.

The line should be solid since the inequality does contain the equal sign.

Pick a test point. Let's use the point (0, 0). Does it satisfy the inequality?

$$(0) \leq 5 \quad \text{or} \quad 0 \leq 5$$

Since the point **does** satisfy the given inequality, shade the side of the line that **does** contain our point.

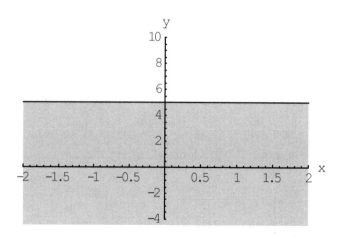

Systems of Linear Inequalities

The solution set of an inequality in two variables is usually an infinite set whose graph is one or more regions of the coordinate plane. The solution set of a **system of inequalities**, such as

$$x + y < 4$$
$$3x - 2y \geq 6$$

is the intersection of the solution sets of each inequality. The solution is best visualized by its graph.

Graphing a System of Inequalities:

To graph the solution set of a system of inequalities, graph both inequalities on the same axes. Then shade the solution set for each inequality, and finally identify the solution of the system by shading heavily the region common to both graphs.

Example 5. Graph:
$$x + 2y \leq 6$$
$$x - y \geq 3$$

Solution: Graph the $x + 2y \leq 6$ by graphing $x + 2y = 6$ using a solid line. Use $(0, 0)$ as the test point, find the half-plane that represents the solution, and shade that side.

Then graph $x - y \geq 3$ by graphing $x - y = 3$ using a solid line. Use $(0, 0)$ as the test point; find the half-plane that represents the solution; and shade that side.

The solution set of the system is the region of the plane that is shaded by **both** inequalities.

Note that the parts of the lines $x + 2y = 6$ and $x - y = 3$ that are included in the combined shaded areas are also within the solution set.

Graph of

$$x + 2y \le 6$$
$$x - y \ge 3$$

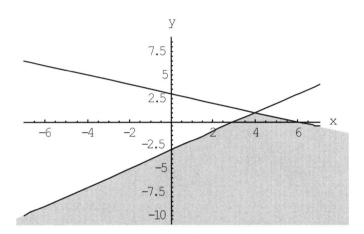

Example 5 can be solved using a graphing calculator. See Chapter 6, Example 48.

Section 5.3 Exercises

Graph:

1. $y > 3x$ 2. $3y < x$

3. $y > x$ 4. $y < x$

5. $x > -4$ 6. $x < 5$

7. $y > 4$ 8. $y < -3$

9. $2x - 3y \leq 6$ 10. $3x + 2y \leq 12$

11. $x \leq -3$ 12. $x \geq 5$

13. $y \leq -1$ 14. $y \geq -2$

Graph each system and then find the solution set:

15.
$$x + 2y > 2$$
$$x - 2y < 4$$

16.
$$2x - y < 4$$
$$x + 3y > -2$$

17.
$$3x - 4y \leq 3$$
$$2x + y \geq -2$$

18.
$$x \leq 4$$
$$y \geq 2$$

Section 5.4 Solving Linear Systems with Matrices

Suppose that you are the owner of a sports store, and you receive the following shipments of golf balls from two golf ball makers: from Willis you receive 2 cases of white balls, 4 cases of yellow balls, and 8 cases of red balls; and from Boyd you receive 4 cases of white balls, 3 cases of yellow balls, and 11 cases of red balls.

We can rewrite the golf ball information in a chart so that it is easier to see.

Golf Balls

Manufacturer	white	yellow	red
Willis	2	4	8
Boyd	4	3	11

We can also remove the names and identifying words and reduce the numbers to an array of numbers that contain the shipment information.

$$\begin{bmatrix} 2 & 4 & 8 \\ 4 & 3 & 11 \end{bmatrix}$$

A rectangular array like this is called a **matrix** (plural matrices).

Properties of a matrix:

Each number in the array is called an **element** of the array.

The **rows** are horizontal, and the **columns** are vertical.

The above matrix has 2 rows and 3 columns and is called a "two by three" matrix.

A matrix with p rows and q columns is said to be a "p by q" matrix.

If the number of rows is equal to the number of columns, the matrix is a **square matrix.**

Matrices are useful in many areas of math, finance and science. Using the computer with matrices we can solve complicated systems of equations.

An **augmented matrix** is a combination of two matrices written as one. An example of an augmented matrix is show below:

$$\left[\begin{array}{cc|c} 1 & 2 & 3 \\ 4 & 5 & 6 \end{array}\right]$$

This is a combination of the two matrices:

$$\begin{bmatrix} 1 & 2 \\ 4 & 5 \end{bmatrix} \quad \text{and} \quad \begin{bmatrix} 3 \\ 6 \end{bmatrix}$$

Row operations on Matrices:

1. Any two rows can be interchanged.

2. All of the elements of a row can be multiplied by the same nonzero constant.

3. One row can be multiplied by a nonzero constant and then added to another row.

Gauss-Jordan Method of Solving Systems:

Let's look at an example to learn about the Gauss-Jordan Method.

Example 1. Use the Gauss-Jordan method to solve the given linear system.

$$3x - y = 3$$
$$4x + 2y = 14$$

Solution:
The equations are in the needed form, so we will use the given equations to write an augmented matrix.

$$\begin{bmatrix} 3 & -1 & | & 3 \\ 4 & 2 & | & 14 \end{bmatrix}$$

We will use row operations to reduce the above matrix to one that looks like:

$$\begin{bmatrix} 1 & 0 & | & j \\ 0 & 1 & | & k \end{bmatrix} \qquad \textbf{where } j \textbf{ and } k \textbf{ are real numbers}$$

From this matrix we can rewrite our equations as

$$x = j$$

$$y = k$$

Begin with the augmented matrix from the given equations:

$$\begin{bmatrix} 3 & -1 & | & 3 \\ 4 & 2 & | & 14 \end{bmatrix} \quad \text{and } \textbf{convert} \text{ to} \quad \begin{bmatrix} 1 & 0 & | & j \\ 0 & 1 & | & k \end{bmatrix}$$

It is easier to work on columns rather than rows. Use row operations to reduce the augmented matrix.

Since the element in row 1, column 1 should be a one, multiply row 1 by 1/3.

$$\begin{bmatrix} 1 & -1/3 & | & 1 \\ 4 & 2 & | & 14 \end{bmatrix}$$

Now, we need a zero as the element in row 2, column 1, so we will multiply row 1 by -4 and add the result to row 2.

$$\begin{bmatrix} 1 & -1/3 & | & 1 \\ 0 & 10/3 & | & 10 \end{bmatrix}$$

Next we will move to column 2 and work on the element in row 2, column 2. We want that element to be a one, so we will multiply row 2 by 3/10.

$$\begin{bmatrix} 1 & -1/3 & | & 1 \\ 0 & 1 & | & 3 \end{bmatrix}$$

Now we want a zero as the element in row 1, column 2. We will multiply row 2 by 1/3 and add it to row 1.

$$\begin{bmatrix} 1 & 0 & | & 2 \\ 0 & 1 & | & 3 \end{bmatrix}$$

This matrix is in the form we want and gives us the solution to the system.

$$x = 2$$
$$y = 3$$

The solution set is (2, 3)

Example 2. Use the Gauss-Jordan method to solve the given system

$$x - y + 5z = -6$$
$$3x + 3y - z = 10$$
$$x + 3y + 2z = 5$$

Solution:
We will begin by writing the augmented matrix.

$$\begin{bmatrix} 1 & -1 & 5 & | & -6 \\ 3 & 3 & -1 & | & 10 \\ 1 & 3 & 2 & | & 5 \end{bmatrix} \quad \text{and } \textbf{convert} \text{ to} \quad \begin{bmatrix} 1 & 0 & 0 & | & j \\ 0 & 1 & 0 & | & k \\ 0 & 0 & 1 & | & m \end{bmatrix}$$

Remember to work on columns. Start with column 1. There is already a one in row 1, column 1, so we will work to get a zero in row 2 of column 1. Multiply row 1 by -3 and add the result to row 2.

$$\begin{bmatrix} 1 & -1 & 5 & | & -6 \\ 0 & 6 & -16 & | & 28 \\ 1 & 3 & 2 & | & 5 \end{bmatrix}$$

Next, we need a zero as the element in column 1, row 3. Multiply row 1 by -1 and adding the result to row 3.

$$\begin{bmatrix} 1 & -1 & 5 & | & -6 \\ 0 & 6 & -16 & | & 28 \\ 0 & 4 & -3 & | & 11 \end{bmatrix}$$

Now we will move to column 2. We need the element in column 2, row 2 to be a one. Divide row 2 by 6.

$$\begin{bmatrix} 1 & -1 & 5 & | & -6 \\ 0 & 1 & -8/3 & | & 14/3 \\ 0 & 4 & -3 & | & 11 \end{bmatrix}$$

Now, we need a zero as the element in row 1, column 2. Add row 2 to row 1 and place the result in row 1.

$$\begin{bmatrix} 1 & 0 & 7/3 & | & -4/3 \\ 0 & 1 & -8/3 & | & 14/3 \\ 0 & 4 & -3 & | & 11 \end{bmatrix}$$

Now, use row operations to change the element in column 2, row 3 to a zero. We will multiply row 2 by -4 and add the result to row 3.

$$\begin{bmatrix} 1 & 0 & 7/3 & | & -4/3 \\ 0 & 1 & -8/3 & | & 14/3 \\ 0 & 0 & 23/3 & | & -23/3 \end{bmatrix}$$

Next, move to column 3. We first need a one as the element in column 3, row 3. We will multiply row 3 by 3/23.

$$\begin{bmatrix} 1 & 0 & 7/3 & | & -4/3 \\ 0 & 1 & -8/3 & | & 14/3 \\ 0 & 0 & 1 & | & -1 \end{bmatrix}$$

We will continue with column 3. We want the element in row 1, column 3 to be a zero. Multiply row 3 by $-7/3$ and add the result to row 1.

$$\begin{bmatrix} 1 & 0 & 0 & | & 1 \\ 0 & 1 & -8/3 & | & 14/3 \\ 0 & 0 & 1 & | & -1 \end{bmatrix}$$

We will work to change the element in column 3, row 2 to a zero. Multiply row 3 by 8/3 and add the result to row 2.

$$\begin{bmatrix} 1 & 0 & 0 & | & 1 \\ 0 & 1 & 0 & | & 2 \\ 0 & 0 & 1 & | & -1 \end{bmatrix}$$

The solution to the system is:

$$x = 1$$
$$y = 2$$
$$z = -1$$

The solution is $(1,\ 2,\ -1)$

Example 3.   Use the Gauss-Jordan method to solve the system

$$x + y = 2$$
$$3x + 3y = 7$$

Solution.
Begin by writing the augmented matrix.

$$\begin{bmatrix} 1 & 1 & | & 2 \\ 3 & 3 & | & 7 \end{bmatrix}$$

Remember to work with columns. There is already a 1 in row 1, column 1, so a zero is needed in row 2 of column 1. Multiply row 1 by -3 and add the result to row 2.

$$\begin{bmatrix} 1 & 1 & | & 2 \\ 0 & 0 & | & 1 \end{bmatrix}$$

Our next step is to get a 1 in column 2, row 2. Because of the zeros, we are unable to do this step.

The second reduced row corresponding equation is:

$$0x + 0y = 1$$

and this equation has no solution, so the solution to the system of equations has no solution. The system is inconsistent.

Row-Echelon Form of a Matrix:

A matrix is in row-echelon form if:

1. Unless the row has all 0's, the first nonzero element in the row is a 1.

2. For any 2 successive rows, the leading 1 in the upper row is to the left of the leading 1 in the lower row.

3. All of the rows that contain only zeros are at the bottom of the matrix.

Example 4. Which of the following matrices are in row-echelon form?

a. $\begin{bmatrix} 1 & -2 & 4 & | & 3 \\ 0 & 2 & 5 & | & 2 \\ 0 & 0 & 1 & | & 1 \end{bmatrix}$
b. $\begin{bmatrix} 1 & 0 & 0 & | & 2 \\ 0 & 0 & 1 & | & 3 \\ 0 & 0 & 0 & | & 0 \end{bmatrix}$
c. $\begin{bmatrix} 1 & 0 & | & 4 \\ 0 & 0 & | & 0 \end{bmatrix}$

d. $\begin{bmatrix} 1 & 0 & 2 & | & 3 \\ 0 & 1 & 1 & | & 2 \\ 0 & 1 & 0 & | & 1 \end{bmatrix}$ e. $\begin{bmatrix} 1 & 2 & 2 & | & 2 \\ 0 & 1 & 3 & | & 3 \\ 0 & 0 & 0 & | & 0 \end{bmatrix}$ f. $\begin{bmatrix} 1 & 0 & 3 & | & 2 \\ 0 & 1 & 2 & | & 3 \\ 0 & 0 & 1 & | & 5 \end{bmatrix}$

Solution: The matrices shown in b, c, e, and f are examples of row-echelon matrices because they follow the rules for such.

The matrix in example a is not in row-echelon form because the leading element in row 2 is not 1.

The matrix in example d is not in row-echelon form because the leading element in row 3 is not to the right of the leading element in row 2.

Section 5.4 Exercises

Write the augmented matrix for the following systems.

1. $2x - y = 4$
   $x + 3y = 4$

2. $x + 4y = 9$
   $3x - 2y = 8$

3. $x + 4y - 2z = 5$
   $x \quad\quad + 3z = 7$
   $2y + z = 4$

4. $3y - z = 5$
   $2x + 2y = 4$
   $x - 3y + 4z = 1$

Solve the equations using the Gauss-Jordan method.

5. $2x + 3y = 7$
   $4x - 2y = 6$

6. $x + y = 4$
   $x - y = 0$

7. $3x + 4y = 4$
   $4x - 2y = -2$

8. $3x - 5y = 2$
   $x + 2y = 8$

9. $3x - 4y = 5$
   $x + 5y = 8$

10. $4x - y = 13$
    $3x + 3y = 6$

11. $3x + 2y - z = 4$
    $4x - y + 2z = 5$
    $2x - y - z = 0$

12. $2x + 3y + 2z = 1$
    $x - 5y + 3z = 7$
    $3x + y + 4z = 5$

13. $2x + 4y - 2z = 8$
    $3x + 2y + z = 0$
    $x + 3y - 3z = 8$

14. $3x + 4y - 2z = 6$
    $4x - 3y + z = 8$
    $x - y + 3z = 2$

15. $2x - y + 5z = 6$
    $x - 2y - 4z = 4$
    $3x - y + 2z = 5$

16. $3x + 3y + 4z = 12$
    $x - y + z = 1$
    $2x + 4y + 2z = 10$

17. $2x + y - z = 5$
    $x + 3y - z = 6$
    $3x - 2y + z = 2$

18. $2x + 3y - z = 5$
    $4x - y - 2x = 3$
    $6x - 3y - 7z = 7$

Section 5.5   Inverse Matrices

Multiplication of Matrices

Each element c_{ij} of the product matrix C of an m x n matrix A and an n x p matrix B is found as follows:

$$c_{ij} = a_{i1}b_{1j} + a_{i2}b_{2j} + a_{i3}b_{3j} + \ldots + a_{in}b_{nj}$$

To accomplish the multiplication for each element, simultaneously move to the right along a row from matrix A and down a column of matrix B, multiplying each pair of elements and then add the products of the pairs.

Example 1. Find the product of the two given matrices:

$$A = \begin{bmatrix} 1 & 3 & -4 \\ 4 & 0 & -2 \end{bmatrix} \quad \text{and} \quad B = \begin{bmatrix} 5 & -4 & 2 & 0 \\ -1 & 6 & 3 & 1 \\ 7 & 0 & 5 & 8 \end{bmatrix}$$

Solution: Matrix A is a 2×3 matrix and B is a 3×4 matrix. The product $C = AB$ is a 2×4 matrix. Use the above rule for finding each element of the matrix C:

Row A	Column B	Element of C
R_1	C_1	$c_{11} = 1*5 + 3*(-1) + (-4)*7 = -26$
R_1	C_2	$c_{12} = 1*(-4) + 3*6 + (-4)*0 = 14$
R_1	C_3	$c_{13} = 1*2 + 3*3 + (-4)*5 = -9$
R_1	C_4	$c_{14} = 1*0 + 3*1 + (-4)*8 = -29$
R_2	C_1	$c_{21} = 4*5 + 0*(-1) + (-2)*7 = 6$
R_2	C_2	$c_{22} = 4*(-4) + 0*6 + (-2)*0 = -16$
R_2	C_3	$c_{23} = 4*2 + 0*3 + (-2)*5 = -2$
R_2	C_4	$c_{24} = 4*0 + 0*1 + (-2)*8 = -16$

285

Thus,

$$AB = \begin{bmatrix} 1 & 3 & -4 \\ 4 & 0 & -2 \end{bmatrix} \begin{bmatrix} 5 & -4 & 2 & 0 \\ -1 & 6 & 3 & 1 \\ 7 & 0 & 5 & 8 \end{bmatrix} = \begin{bmatrix} -26 & 14 & -9 & -29 \\ 6 & -16 & -2 & -16 \end{bmatrix}$$

Example 1 can be solved using a graphing calculator. See Chapter 6, Example 49.

We know that the identity property of real numbers states that for any number n,

$$(n)(1) = n \qquad \text{and} \qquad (1)(n) = n$$

The same idea is true for matrices. If I is an identity matrix, then it follows that for any square matrix A plus the fact that A and I must be of the same order:

$$AI = A \qquad \text{and} \qquad IA = A$$

Identity Matrices

The symbol I_n is used to denote the square matrix of order n that has 1 in each position on the main diagonal and 0 everywhere else.

$$I_2 = \begin{bmatrix} 1 & 0 \\ 0 & 1 \end{bmatrix} \qquad I_3 = \begin{bmatrix} 1 & 0 & 0 \\ 0 & 1 & 0 \\ 0 & 0 & 1 \end{bmatrix}$$

From the identity rule for a matrix , we know that

$$AI_n = A = I_n A$$

Inverse of a Matrix

Inverse of a matrix:

If A is a square matrix of order n, and if there exists a matrix B such that

$$AB = I_n = BA$$

then B is the <u>inverse</u> of A and is written as A^{-1}

<u>To find the inverse of a square matrix</u>:

1. Make a matrix that is a combination of the given matrix followed by an identity matrix of the same order.

2. Use elementary row operations to change the new matrix so that the identity matrix portion appears as the first matrix of the combination.

3. The second section of the combined matrix is then the inverse.

Example 2. Find the inverse of the matrix A.

$$A = \begin{bmatrix} 2 & 4 \\ 1 & 5 \end{bmatrix}$$

Solution: We begin by combining matrix A with the I_2

$$\left[\begin{array}{cc|cc} 2 & 4 & 1 & 0 \\ 1 & 5 & 0 & 1 \end{array}\right]$$

Now use row operations to convert the first two columns of the combined matrix into the identity matrix.

First switch rows 1 and 2 so that the element in row 1, column 1 will be a 1.

$$\left[\begin{array}{cc|cc} 1 & 5 & 0 & 1 \\ 2 & 4 & 1 & 0 \end{array}\right]$$

A zero is needed as the first element in row 2, column 1. Multiply row 1 by -2 and add the result to row 2.

$$\begin{bmatrix} 1 & 5 & | & 0 & 1 \\ 0 & -6 & | & 1 & -2 \end{bmatrix}$$

Next, we move to column 2.

A one is needed as the element in row 2, column 2. Divide row 2 by -6.

$$\begin{bmatrix} 1 & 5 & | & 0 & 1 \\ 0 & 1 & | & -1/6 & 1/3 \end{bmatrix}$$

A zero is needed as the element in row 1, column 2. Multiply row 2 by -5 and add the result to row 1.

$$\begin{bmatrix} 1 & 0 & | & 5/6 & -2/3 \\ 0 & 1 & | & -1/6 & 1/3 \end{bmatrix}$$

The first portion of this matrix is now the identity matrix. The second portion of the matrix is the inverse of the original matrix.

$$A^{-1} = \begin{bmatrix} 5/6 & -2/3 \\ -1/6 & 1/3 \end{bmatrix}$$

Example 2 can be solved using a graphing calculator. See Chapter 6, Example 50.

Example 3. Find A^{-1} if $A = \begin{bmatrix} 1 & 0 & 1 \\ 2 & -2 & -1 \\ 3 & 0 & 0 \end{bmatrix}$

Solution: Write the combination matrix:

$$\begin{bmatrix} 1 & 0 & 1 & | & 1 & 0 & 0 \\ 2 & -2 & -1 & | & 0 & 1 & 0 \\ 3 & 0 & 0 & | & 0 & 0 & 1 \end{bmatrix}$$

Begin with column 1. Since there is already a 1 at row 1, column 1, look at row 2, column 1. This element should be zero. Multiply row 1 by -2 and add the result to row 2.

$$\left[\begin{array}{ccc|ccc} 1 & 0 & 1 & 1 & 0 & 0 \\ 0 & -2 & -3 & -2 & 1 & 0 \\ 3 & 0 & 0 & 0 & 0 & 1 \end{array}\right]$$

The element in row 3, column 1 should be zero. Multiply row 1 by -3 and add the result to row 3.

$$\left[\begin{array}{ccc|ccc} 1 & 0 & 1 & 1 & 0 & 0 \\ 0 & -2 & -3 & -2 & 1 & 0 \\ 0 & 0 & -3 & -3 & 0 & 1 \end{array}\right]$$

Move to column 2. To get a one as the element in row 2, column 2, multiply row 2 by $-1/2$.

$$\left[\begin{array}{ccc|ccc} 1 & 0 & 1 & 1 & 0 & 0 \\ 0 & 1 & 3/2 & 1 & -1/2 & 0 \\ 0 & 0 & -3 & -3 & 0 & 1 \end{array}\right]$$

Move to column 3. To get the element in row 3, column 3 to be a one, divide row 3 by $-1/3$.

$$\left[\begin{array}{ccc|ccc} 1 & 0 & 1 & 1 & 0 & 0 \\ 0 & 1 & 3/2 & 1 & -1/2 & 0 \\ 0 & 0 & 1 & 1 & 0 & -1/3 \end{array}\right]$$

Next we want a zero in row 1, column 3. Multiply row 3 by -1 and add the result to the first row.

$$\left[\begin{array}{ccc|ccc} 1 & 0 & 0 & 0 & 0 & 1/3 \\ 0 & 1 & 3/2 & 1 & -1/2 & 0 \\ 0 & 0 & 1 & 1 & 0 & -1/3 \end{array}\right]$$

A zero is needed as the element of row 2, column 3. Multiply row 3 by $-3/2$ and add the result to row 2.

$$\left[\begin{array}{ccc|ccc} 1 & 0 & 0 & 0 & 0 & 1/3 \\ 0 & 1 & 0 & -1/2 & -1/2 & 1/2 \\ 0 & 0 & 1 & 1 & 0 & -1/3 \end{array}\right]$$

The identity matrix elements are now in place, and the inverse is

$$A^{-1} = \left[\begin{array}{ccc} 0 & 0 & 1/3 \\ -1/2 & -1/2 & 1/2 \\ 1 & 0 & -1/3 \end{array}\right]$$

Example 3 may be solved using a graphing calculator. See Chapter 6, Example 51.

Not all matrices have inverses. When trying to find the identity matrix on the left side of an augmented matrix and a row of only zeros occurs, then an inverse matrix does not exist.

Using Matrix Inverses to Solve a System of Equations:

<u>The Inverse Method</u>:

If we are given a system of two linear equations with two variables

$$a_{11}x + a_{12}y = r_1$$
$$a_{21}x + a_{22}y = r_2$$

This system can be expressed in terms of matrices as

$$\left[\begin{array}{c} a_{11}x + a_{12}y \\ a_{21}x + a_{22}y \end{array}\right] = \left[\begin{array}{c} r_1 \\ r_2 \end{array}\right]$$

Let $A = \begin{bmatrix} a_{11} & a_{12} \\ a_{21} & a_{22} \end{bmatrix}$ $X = \begin{bmatrix} x \\ y \end{bmatrix}$ and $C = \begin{bmatrix} r_1 \\ r_2 \end{bmatrix}$

We can write the system written in <u>matrix form</u>.

$$AX = C$$

If the inverse of A does exist, we can rewrite the above matrix form as

$$X = A^{-1}C$$

and thus we can find the solution (x,y) to the system.

Example 4. Solve the following system of equations.

$$x - y + z = 4$$
$$2x + y + 3z = 7$$
$$-x - 4y - z = 1$$

Solution: Let

$$A = \begin{bmatrix} 1 & -1 & 1 \\ 2 & 1 & 3 \\ -1 & -4 & -1 \end{bmatrix} \quad X = \begin{bmatrix} x \\ y \\ z \end{bmatrix} \quad C = \begin{bmatrix} 4 \\ 7 \\ 1 \end{bmatrix}$$

Use the method described earlier to find the inverse matrix A^{-1}.

$$A^{-1} = \frac{1}{5}\begin{bmatrix} 11 & -5 & -4 \\ -1 & 0 & -1 \\ -7 & 5 & 0 \end{bmatrix}$$

Then, using $X = A^{-1}C$ we have

$$\begin{bmatrix} x \\ y \\ z \end{bmatrix} = \frac{1}{5} \begin{bmatrix} 11 & -5 & -4 \\ -1 & 0 & -1 \\ -7 & 5 & 3 \end{bmatrix} \begin{bmatrix} 4 \\ 7 \\ 1 \end{bmatrix} = \begin{bmatrix} 1 \\ -1 \\ 2 \end{bmatrix}$$

Multiply the matrices on the right side to find the solution.

The solution to the given system is (1, −1, 2)

Example 3 can be solved using a graphing calculator. See Chapter 6, Example 51.

Section 5.5 Exercises

Find the inverse of the following matrices if it exists:

1. $\begin{bmatrix} 1 & -1 \\ 2 & 0 \end{bmatrix}$

2. $\begin{bmatrix} -1 & -2 \\ 3 & 4 \end{bmatrix}$

3. $\begin{bmatrix} 3 & -1 \\ -5 & 2 \end{bmatrix}$

4. $\begin{bmatrix} 2 & -1 \\ 4 & 1 \end{bmatrix}$

5. $\begin{bmatrix} 1 & 2 \\ 3 & 4 \end{bmatrix}$

6. $\begin{bmatrix} 5 & 10 \\ -3 & -6 \end{bmatrix}$

7. $\begin{bmatrix} 1 & 2 \\ 3/2 & 3 \end{bmatrix}$

8. $\begin{bmatrix} 2 & 4 \\ 1 & 0 \end{bmatrix}$

9. $\begin{bmatrix} 1 & -1 & 1 \\ 2 & 1 & 0 \\ 1 & 0 & 1 \end{bmatrix}$

10. $\begin{bmatrix} 1 & 3 & 0 \\ 1 & 5 & 3 \\ 0 & 0 & 1 \end{bmatrix}$

11. $\begin{bmatrix} 2 & 2 & 2 \\ 4 & 5 & 0 \\ 0 & -1 & 3 \end{bmatrix}$

12. $\begin{bmatrix} -1 & 1 & -2 \\ 2 & 0 & 4 \\ 3 & 1 & 5 \end{bmatrix}$

13. $\begin{bmatrix} -2 & -7/2 & 2 \\ 1 & 1/2 & 0 \\ 1 & 2 & -1 \end{bmatrix}$

14. $\begin{bmatrix} 1 & 0 & 1/2 \\ 2 & 3 & 1 \\ 4 & 0 & 2 \end{bmatrix}$

15. $\begin{bmatrix} 2 & 0 & 1 \\ 1 & 2 & 2 \\ 4 & 0 & 2 \end{bmatrix}$

Solve the following systems using matrix inverses.

16. $\begin{aligned} 2x + y &= 5 \\ 3x - y &= 5 \end{aligned}$

17. $\begin{aligned} 2x = 3y &= 3 \\ 4x - y &= 13 \end{aligned}$

Section 5.6 Determinants

Every square matrix A is associated with a real number called the determinant of A.

The determinant of a 2 x 2 matrix A

$$A = \begin{bmatrix} a_{11} & a_{12} \\ a_{21} & a_{22} \end{bmatrix},$$

is defined as:

$$\delta(A) = \begin{vmatrix} a_{11} & a_{12} \\ a_{21} & a_{22} \end{vmatrix} = a_{11}a_{22} - a_{21}a_{12}$$

Example 1. If $B = \begin{bmatrix} -2 & 4 \\ 6 & 8 \end{bmatrix}$

Find $\delta(B)$ which is the determinant of matrix B.

Solution: $\delta(B) = \begin{bmatrix} -2 & 4 \\ 6 & 8 \end{bmatrix} = -2(8) - 6(4) = -40$

Example 1 can be solved using a graphing calculator. See Chapter 6, Example 52.

294

The above definition of a determinant can be extended to a 3 X 3 matrix as well.

Definition of Minors and Cofactors:

If $A = (a_{ij})$ is a square matrix of order n with n greater than 1, then:

1. The <u>minor</u> M_{ij} of the element a_{ij} is the determinant of the matrix of order $n-1$ obtained by deleting row i and column j.

2. The <u>cofactor</u> A_{ij} of the element a_{ij} is $A_{ij} = (-1)^{i+j} M_{ij}$

The above definition of a minor says that to find the minor of any element we delete the row and column in which the element appears and find the determinant of the resulting square matrix.

Example 2: Examples of minors and cofactors.

Matrix	Minor	Cofactor
$\begin{bmatrix} a_{11} & a_{12} & a_{13} \\ a_{21} & a_{22} & a_{23} \\ a_{31} & a_{32} & a_{33} \end{bmatrix}$	$M_{11} = \begin{vmatrix} a_{22} & a_{23} \\ a_{32} & a_{33} \end{vmatrix}$ $= a_{22}a_{33} - a_{32}a_{23}$	$A_{11} = (-1)^{1+1} M_{11} = M_{11}$
$\begin{bmatrix} a_{11} & a_{12} & a_{13} \\ a_{21} & a_{22} & a_{23} \\ a_{31} & a_{32} & a_{33} \end{bmatrix}$	$M_{12} = \begin{vmatrix} a_{21} & a_{23} \\ a_{31} & a_{33} \end{vmatrix}$ $= a_{21}a_{33} - a_{31}a_{23}$	$A_{12} = (-1)^{1+2} M_{12} = -M_{12}$
$\begin{bmatrix} a_{11} & a_{12} & a_{13} \\ a_{21} & a_{22} & a_{23} \\ a_{31} & a_{32} & a_{33} \end{bmatrix}$	$M_{23} = \begin{vmatrix} a_{11} & a_{12} \\ a_{31} & a_{32} \end{vmatrix}$ $= a_{11}a_{32} - a_{31}a_{12}$	$A_{23} = (-1)^{2+3} M_{23} = -M_{23}$

There are six other minors that can be obtained in a similar manner.

295

To remember the sign associated with each cofactor, look at the following chart.

$$\begin{bmatrix} + & - & + & - & \dots \\ - & + & - & + & \dots \\ + & - & + & - & \dots \\ - & + & - & + & \dots \\ \cdot & \cdot & \cdot & \cdot \\ \cdot & \cdot & \cdot & \cdot \\ \cdot & \cdot & \cdot & \cdot \end{bmatrix}$$

Example 3. Given matrix A

$$A = \begin{bmatrix} 1 & -2 & 3 \\ 4 & 2 & 5 \\ 2 & -7 & 0 \end{bmatrix} \quad \text{find } M_{11}, \ M_{21}, \ M_{22}, \ A_{11}, \ A_{21}, \ A_{22}$$

Solution : Delete the appropriate rows and columns of A

$$M_{11} = \begin{vmatrix} 2 & 5 \\ -7 & 0 \end{vmatrix} = (2)(0) - (-7)(5) = 35$$

$$M_{21} = \begin{vmatrix} -2 & 3 \\ -7 & 0 \end{vmatrix} = (-2)(0) - (-7)(3) = 21$$

$$M_{22} = \begin{vmatrix} 1 & 3 \\ 2 & 0 \end{vmatrix} = (1)(0) - (2)(3) = -6$$

$$A_{11} = (-1)^{1+1} M_{11} = (1)(35) = 35$$

$$A_{21} = (-1)^{2+1} M_{21} = (-1)(21) = -21$$

$$A_{22} = (-1)^{2+2} M_{22} = (1)(-6) = -6$$

The determinant $\delta(A)$ of a square matrix of order 3:

$$\delta(A) = \begin{vmatrix} a_{11} & a_{12} & a_{13} \\ a_{21} & a_{22} & a_{23} \\ a_{31} & a_{32} & a_{33} \end{vmatrix} = a_{11}A_{11} + a_{12}A_{12} + a_{13}A_{13}$$

Note that cofactors $A_{11} = (-1)^{1+1}M_{11} = M_{11}$, $A_{12} = (-1)^{1+2}M_{12} = -M_{12}$, and $A_{13} = (-1)^{1+3}M_{13} = M_{13}$. We can write the above definition of the determinant.

The determinant $\delta(A)$ of a square matrix of order 3:

$$\delta(A) = a_{11}M_{11} - a_{12}M_{12} + a_{13}M_{13}$$

Example 4. Given matrix A. Find the determinant of A.

$$A = \begin{bmatrix} -1 & 3 & 2 \\ 1 & 4 & 0 \\ 3 & -2 & 5 \end{bmatrix}$$

Solution: We will use the definition: $\delta(A) = a_{11}M_{11} - a_{12}M_{12} + a_{13}M_{13}$

$$\delta(A) = -1\begin{bmatrix} 4 & 0 \\ -2 & 5 \end{bmatrix} - 3\begin{vmatrix} 1 & 0 \\ 3 & 5 \end{vmatrix} + 2\begin{vmatrix} 1 & 4 \\ 3 & -2 \end{vmatrix}$$

$$= -1(4*5-(-2*0)) - 3(1*5-3*0) + 2(1*(-2)-3*4)$$

$$= -1(20) - 3(5) + 2(-14) = -20 - 15 - 28 = -63$$

Example 4 can be solved using a graphing calculator. See Chapter 6, Example 53.

Cramer's Rule

We have already learned how to solve systems of linear equations using the elimination method.   We can also use determinants to solve a system of linear equations.

Given a general system of two linear equations in two variables:

$$a_1 x + b_1 y = c_1$$
$$a_2 x + b_2 y = c_2$$

To eliminate y and solve for x, we multiply both sides of equation (1) above by b_2 and equation (2) above by $-b_1$ and then add the two new equations

$$a_1 b_2 x + b_1 b_2 y = c_1 b_2$$
$$\underline{- a_2 b_1 x - b_1 b_2 y = -c_2 b_1}$$
$$(a_1 b_2 - a_2 b_1)x \quad = c_1 b_2 - c_2 b_1$$

Solve for x

$$x = \frac{c_1 b_2 - c_2 b_1}{a_1 b_2 - a_2 b_1}$$

To eliminate x and solve for y, multiply both sides of equation (1) by $-a_2$ and equation (2) by a_1 and then add the two new equations.

$$- a_1 a_2 x - a_2 b_1 y = - a_2 c_1$$
$$\underline{a_1 a_2 x + a_1 b_2 y = \quad a_1 c_2}$$
$$(a_1 b_2 - a_2 b_1)y = a_1 c_2 - a_2 c_1$$

Solve for y

$$y = \frac{a_1 c_2 - a_2 c_1}{a_1 b_2 - a_2 b_1}$$

Both numerators and the common denominator of these values for x and y can be written as determinants since

$$c_1 b_2 - c_2 b_1 = \begin{vmatrix} c_1 & b_1 \\ c_2 & b_2 \end{vmatrix} \; ; \qquad a_1 c_2 - a_2 c_1 = \begin{vmatrix} a_1 & c_1 \\ a_2 & c_2 \end{vmatrix} \; ; \qquad \text{and} \qquad a_1 b_2 - a_2 b_1 = \begin{vmatrix} a_1 & b_1 \\ a_2 & b_2 \end{vmatrix}$$

Cramer's rule is the result.

Cramer's Rule for 2 x 2 Systems:

Given the system:
$$a_1 x + b_1 y = c_1$$
$$a_2 x + b_2 y = c_2$$

With $a_1 b_2 - a_2 b_1 \neq 0$,

$$x = \frac{\begin{vmatrix} c_1 & b_1 \\ c_2 & b_2 \end{vmatrix}}{\begin{vmatrix} a_1 & b_1 \\ a_2 & b_2 \end{vmatrix}} \qquad \text{and} \qquad y = \frac{\begin{vmatrix} a_1 & c_1 \\ a_2 & c_2 \end{vmatrix}}{\begin{vmatrix} a_1 & b_1 \\ a_2 & b_2 \end{vmatrix}}$$

A shorthand way of writing these two solutions is shown.

$$\begin{vmatrix} a_1 & b_1 \\ a_2 & b_2 \end{vmatrix} = D \qquad \begin{vmatrix} c_1 & b_1 \\ c_2 & b_2 \end{vmatrix} = D_x \qquad \begin{vmatrix} a_1 & c_1 \\ a_2 & c_2 \end{vmatrix} = D_y$$

Then

$$x = \frac{D_x}{D} \qquad \text{and} \qquad y = \frac{D_y}{D} \qquad \text{where } D \neq 0$$

Example 5. Solve the following system using Cramer's rule.

$$4x + 6y = 1$$
$$3x + 5y = -2$$

Solution: Using Cramer's rule, we will solve for D, D_x, and D_y.

$$D = \begin{vmatrix} 4 & 6 \\ 3 & 5 \end{vmatrix} = 4 * 5 - 3 * 6 = 20 - 18 = 2$$

$$D_x = \begin{vmatrix} 1 & 6 \\ -2 & 5 \end{vmatrix} = 1 * 5 - (-2) * 6 = 5 + 12 = 17$$

$$D_y = \begin{vmatrix} 4 & 1 \\ 3 & -2 \end{vmatrix} = 4 * (-2) - 3 * 1 = -8 - 3 = -11$$

By Cramer's rule:

$$x = \frac{D_x}{D} = \frac{17}{2} \qquad\qquad y = \frac{D_y}{D} = \frac{-11}{2}$$

The solution set to the given system is: $(17/2, \ -11/2)$.

Check:

$$\begin{array}{l} 4x + 6y = 1 \\ 3x + 5y = -2 \end{array} \quad \text{using } x = 17/2, \ \ y = -11/2$$

Equation 1:

$$4(17/2) + 6(-11/2) = 68/2 + -66/2 = 2/2 = 1$$

Equation 2:

$$3(17/2) + 5(-11/2) = 51/2 - 55/2 = -4/2 = -2$$

Cramer's rule can be generalized to larger systems of equations.

Cramer's Rule for 3 x 3 Systems:

$$a_1 x + b_1 y + c_1 z = d_1$$

Given the system:
$$a_2 x + b_2 y + c_2 z = d_2$$
$$a_3 x + b_3 y + c_3 z = d_3$$

With

$$D_x = \begin{vmatrix} d_1 & b_1 & c_1 \\ d_2 & b_2 & c_2 \\ d_3 & b_3 & c_3 \end{vmatrix} \qquad D_y = \begin{vmatrix} a_1 & d_1 & c_1 \\ a_2 & d_2 & c_2 \\ a_3 & d_3 & c_3 \end{vmatrix}$$

$$D_z = \begin{vmatrix} a_1 & b_1 & d_1 \\ a_2 & b_2 & d_2 \\ a_3 & b_3 & d_3 \end{vmatrix} \qquad D = \begin{vmatrix} a_1 & b_1 & c_1 \\ a_2 & b_2 & c_2 \\ a_3 & b_3 & c_3 \end{vmatrix}$$

Then

$$x = \frac{D_x}{D} \qquad y = \frac{D_y}{D} \qquad \text{and} \quad z = \frac{D_z}{D}$$

Example 6. Solve the following system using Cramer's rule.

$$2x - y + 4z = -2$$
$$3x + 2y - z = -3$$
$$x + 4y + 2z = 17$$

Solution;

Find $D, D_x, D_y, \text{and } D_z$

$$D = \begin{vmatrix} 2 & -1 & 4 \\ 3 & 2 & -1 \\ 1 & 4 & 2 \end{vmatrix}$$

$$= 2(2*2 - 4*(-1)) - (-1)(3*2 - 1*(-1)) + 4(3*4 - 1*2) = 63$$

$$D_x = \begin{vmatrix} -2 & -1 & 4 \\ -3 & 2 & -1 \\ 17 & 4 & 2 \end{vmatrix}$$

$$= -2(2*2 - 4(-1)) + 1((-3)2 - 17(-1)) + 4((-3)4 - 17*2) = -189$$

Using the same process, we can find D_y and D_z.

$$D_y = \begin{vmatrix} 2 & -2 & 4 \\ 3 & -3 & -1 \\ 1 & 17 & 2 \end{vmatrix} = 252$$

$$D_z = \begin{vmatrix} 2 & -1 & -2 \\ 3 & 2 & -3 \\ 1 & 4 & 17 \end{vmatrix} = 126$$

Using Cramer's rule:

$$x = \frac{D_x}{D} = \frac{-189}{63} = -3$$

$$y = \frac{D_y}{D} = \frac{252}{63} = 4$$

$$z = \frac{D_z}{D} = \frac{126}{63} = 2$$

The solution is: $(-3, 4, 2)$.

Section 5.6 Exercises:

Find the value of the determinant:

1. $\begin{vmatrix} -3 & \sqrt{6} \\ -\sqrt{6} & 2 \end{vmatrix}$

2. $\begin{vmatrix} \sqrt{2} & -1 \\ 5 & 2 \end{vmatrix}$

3. $\begin{vmatrix} x^2 & 3 \\ x & x^2 \end{vmatrix}$

4. $\begin{vmatrix} t^3 & -1 \\ t^2 & 2 \end{vmatrix}$

5. $\begin{vmatrix} -3 & -2 & 4 \\ 2 & -1 & 2 \\ -1 & 2 & 2 \end{vmatrix}$

6. $\begin{vmatrix} p & -2 & 0 \\ 1 & p & 1 \\ 3 & p & 2 \end{vmatrix}$

7. $\begin{vmatrix} s & 5 & -1 \\ 2 & s & -1 \\ 3 & 2 & -2 \end{vmatrix}$

8. $\begin{vmatrix} y^2 & y & -1 \\ y & 1 & -1 \\ 1 & 2 & 2 \end{vmatrix}$

Answer the following questions using the given matrix.

$$B = \begin{bmatrix} 6 & -2 & 3 \\ 2 & 1 & 0 \\ 1 & -1 & 2 \end{bmatrix}$$

9. Find $M_{12}, M_{23},$ *and* M_{31}

10. Find $M_{22}, M_{33},$ *and* M_{11}

11. Find $B_{12}, B_{23},$ *and* B_{31}

12. Find $B_{22}, B_{33},$ *and* B_{11}

13. Find the determinant of B

Solve using Cramer's rule.

14. $\begin{array}{l} 2x - 3y = 4 \\ x + 2y = 6 \end{array}$

15. $\begin{array}{l} 4x - 3y = -3 \\ 7x + 2y = 6 \end{array}$

16. $\begin{array}{l} 4x + 2y = 8 \\ -5x - 3y = -12 \end{array}$

17. $\begin{array}{l} 3x + 4y = 2 \\ 5x - 7y = -2 \end{array}$

18. $\begin{array}{l} 3x - 5y = 2 \\ 7x + 2y = 9 \end{array}$

19. $\begin{array}{l} x + y - z = -2 \\ 2x - y + z = -5 \\ x - 2y + 3z = 4 \end{array}$

20. $\begin{array}{l} x + 2y = 10 \\ 3x + 4z = 7 \\ -y - z = 1 \end{array}$

Chapter 5 Summary

Solving Systems of linear equations:
1. Graph both equations and find the point of intersection.
2. Use the Substitution Method.
3. Use the Addition Method.

Substitution Method:
1. Solve one of the equations for one of the variables.
   2. Substitute this solution into the other equation and thus get an equation in only one variable.
3. Find the solution to this new equation found in step 2.
4, Substitute the solution found in step 3 back into one of the original equations to get the value of the other variable.
5. Check the solution in both of the given equations.

Addition Method:
1. Multiply the equations on both sides by suitable numbers, so that when the equations are added, one of the variables is eliminated.
2. Add the two new equations.
3. The result is a new equation in only one variable.
4. Solve this single variable equation.
5. Substitute the solution back into one of the original equations to find the value of the second variable.
6. Check the solutions in both of the given equations.

To Solve a System with Three Variables:
1. Eliminate the same variable from each of two pairs of equations.
2. Then using the resulting equations, eliminate another variable.
3. The result of step 2 will be an equation with only one variable.
4. Solve this equation for the value of the variable.
5. Substitute this value in one of the equations found in step 1.
6. Solve for a second variable.
7. Substitute both of the values of the variables back into one of the original equations to find the value of the third variable.
8. It is helpful to number the equations as you go.

Steps for graphing an inequality with two variables:

1. Graph the line that would result if the inequality sign were changed to an = sign.
2. The line will divide the graph into 2 half-planes. One of these is the solution set.
3. To determine which half-plane (the one above or below the line) is the solution, pick a test point and see if it satisfies the inequality given.
4. If the test point satisfies the given inequality, shade the half-plane that includes the point.
5. If the test point does not satisfy the given inequality, shade the other side of the line.
6. Make the line a solid line if the inequality symbol is either $\geq$ or $\leq$.
7. Make the line a dotted line if the inequality symbol is either $>$ or $<$.

Row operations on Matrices:

1. Any two rows can be interchanged.
2. All of the elements of a row can be multiplied by the same nonzero constant.
3. One row can be multiplied by a nonzero constant and then added to another row.

Row-Echelon Form of a Matrix:

A matrix is in row-echelon form if:
1. Unless the row has all 0's, the first nonzero element in the row is a 1.
2. For any 2 successive rows, the leading 1 in the upper row is to the left of the leading 1 in the lower row.
3. All of the rows that contain only zeros are at the bottom of the matrix.

To find the inverse of a square matrix:

1. Make a matrix that is a combination of the given matrix followed by an identity matrix of the same order.
2. Use elementary row operations to change the new matrix so that the identity matrix portion appears as the first matrix of the combination.
3. The second section of the combined matrix is the inverse.

Matrix Solution of Systems of Equations
For a system of n equations, write in Matrix Form:
$$AX = B$$
If the matrix has an inverse, then
$$X = A^{-1}B$$

Determinant
The determinant of a **2 x 2** matrix A
$$A = \begin{bmatrix} a_{11} & a_{12} \\ a_{21} & a_{22} \end{bmatrix},$$

is defined as
$$\delta(A) = \begin{vmatrix} a_{11} & a_{12} \\ a_{21} & a_{22} \end{vmatrix} = a_{11}a_{22} - a_{21}a_{12}$$

The determinant $\delta(A)$ of a square matrix of order 3:

$$\delta(A) = \begin{vmatrix} a_{11} & a_{12} & a_{13} \\ a_{21} & a_{22} & a_{23} \\ a_{31} & a_{32} & a_{33} \end{vmatrix} = a_{11}A_{11} + a_{12}A_{12} + a_{13}A_{13}$$

Cramer's Rule for 2 x 2 Systems:

Given the system:
$$a_1 x + b_1 y = c_1$$
$$a_2 x + b_2 y = c_2$$

With $a_1 b_2 - a_2 b_1 \neq 0,$

$$x = \frac{\begin{vmatrix} c_1 & b_1 \\ c_2 & b_2 \end{vmatrix}}{\begin{vmatrix} a_1 & b_1 \\ a_2 & b_2 \end{vmatrix}} \qquad \text{and} \qquad y = \frac{\begin{vmatrix} a_1 & c_1 \\ a_2 & c_2 \end{vmatrix}}{\begin{vmatrix} a_1 & b_1 \\ a_2 & b_2 \end{vmatrix}}$$

A shorthand way of writing these two solutions is shown.

$$\begin{vmatrix} a_1 & b_1 \\ a_2 & b_2 \end{vmatrix} = D \qquad \begin{vmatrix} c_1 & b_1 \\ c_2 & b_2 \end{vmatrix} = D_x \qquad \begin{vmatrix} a_1 & c_1 \\ a_2 & c_2 \end{vmatrix} = D_y$$

Then

$$x = \frac{D_x}{D} \qquad \textbf{and} \qquad y = \frac{D_y}{D} \qquad \textbf{where } D \neq 0$$

Cramer's Rule for 3 x 3 Systems:

Given the system:
$$a_1 x + b_1 y + c_1 z = d_1$$
$$a_2 x + b_2 y + c_2 z = d_2$$
$$a_3 x + b_3 y + c_3 z = d_3$$

With

$$D_x = \begin{vmatrix} d_1 & b_1 & c_1 \\ d_2 & b_2 & c_2 \\ d_3 & b_3 & c_3 \end{vmatrix} \qquad D_y = \begin{vmatrix} a_1 & d_1 & c_1 \\ a_2 & d_2 & c_2 \\ a_3 & d_3 & c_3 \end{vmatrix}$$

$$D_z = \begin{vmatrix} a_1 & b_1 & d_1 \\ a_2 & b_2 & d_2 \\ a_3 & b_3 & d_3 \end{vmatrix} \qquad D = \begin{vmatrix} a_1 & b_1 & c_1 \\ a_2 & b_2 & c_2 \\ a_3 & b_3 & c_3 \end{vmatrix}$$

$$x = \frac{D_x}{D} \qquad y = \frac{D_y}{D} \qquad \textbf{and} \quad z = \frac{D_z}{D}$$

Chapter 5 Review

Graph the following:

1. $2x - 3y < 5$
   $x + 2y > 3$

2. $x \geq y$
   $x + y \leq 0$

Solve:

3. $\begin{array}{l} x - 3y = -1 \\ 2x + 2y = 6 \end{array}$

4. $\begin{array}{l} 2x + 3y = -1 \\ x - 2y = -4 \end{array}$

5. $\begin{array}{l} 4x + 2y - 2z = 4 \\ 3x + 9y + 6z = 3 \\ 2x + 2y + 2z = 4 \end{array}$

6. $\begin{array}{l} 2x + y + z = 9 \\ -x - y + z = 1 \\ 6x - 2y + 2z = 18 \end{array}$

Write an equivalent matrix equation. Solve the system of equations using the inverse of the coefficient matrix.

7. $\begin{array}{l} 4x + 6y = 14 \\ 2x - y = 3 \end{array}$

8. $\begin{array}{l} 2x + 3y - 4z = 6 \\ 3x - y + 2z = 1 \\ -x + 4y - 3z = 5 \end{array}$

Find the determinant:

9. $\begin{vmatrix} 7 & -2 \\ 3 & -2 \end{vmatrix}$

10. $\begin{vmatrix} 1 & -2 & 0 \\ 2 & 1 & 4 \\ 3 & 3 & 1 \end{vmatrix}$

11. $\begin{vmatrix} -2 & 3 & 1 \\ 3 & -1 & 4 \\ -1 & 1 & 5 \end{vmatrix}$

Solve using Cramer's rule:

12. $\begin{array}{l} 2x + 3y = 1 \\ x - 4y = -1 \end{array}$

13. $\begin{array}{l} 2x - 4y = 0 \\ 5x - 6y = 4 \end{array}$

14. $\begin{array}{l} 3x - y + 2z = 4 \\ 4x + 6y - 3z = 7 \\ 5x - 4z + 3y = 4 \end{array}$

15. $\begin{array}{l} 5x - y + 3z = 8 \\ 3x + 7y - 5z = 20 \\ 4x - 3y + 7z = 2 \end{array}$

16. $\begin{array}{l} x + 2y = 7 \\ 4x - 3y = 1 \end{array}$

17. $\begin{array}{l} 5x - 3y = -1 \\ 4x + 7y = 2 \end{array}$

308

CHAPTER 6
SOLUTIONS USING GRAPHING CALCULATOR

Example 1:
   If $f(x) = 2x^2 - 2x + 4$ find each of the following:
      a. $f(-2)$
      b. $f(0)$

We can find values for functions using "$y =.....$" rather than "$f(x) = ...$". Enter the equation into $Y_1 =$ and then you can either use the TABLE feature in the ASK mode or we can use the VALUE feature found in the CALC menu.
With both of these we get $f(-2) = 16$ and $f(0) = 4$

Example 2:
Linear Regression Problem: Find the line of best fit that approximates the following data on world record times for the women's 100 meter dash.

Year	Time in Seconds
1952	11.4
1960	11.3
1972	11.07
1984	10.76

Enter the data: Put years in L1, times in L2 using the TABLE feature.

Clear all Y assignments and lists.
A list can be cleared by placing the cursor on the list name and pressing:

      CLEAR   and   ▼

Use the following: STAT   1
      1952   ENTER   1960   ENTER
      1972   ENTER   1984   ENTER
      ▲ 4times   ▶
      11.4   ENTER   11.3   ENTER
      11.07   ENTER   10.76 ENTER

Now, find the best regression line:
      STAT ▶ 4
      VARS ▶ 1   1   ENTER

Screen will show: LinReg($ax+b$) Y$_1$

$$\cdots$$

LinReg
y=$ax+b$
a=−0.0201190476
b=50.70666667

From this screen, we are able to see that the regression line has the approximate equation
$y = -0.02x + 50.71$

Example 3:
Relative Maxima and Minima Problem:

Use a graphing calculator to determine any relative maxima or minima of the function:
$$f(x) = 0.2x^3 - 0.8x^2 - 0.2x + 4$$

Solution:
First, graph the function letting $Y_1 = 0.2x^3 - 0.8x^2 - 0.2x + 4$.

Adjust the window until a nice curve is seen.

Use the MAXIMUM and MINIMUM keys found in the CALC menu to find each relative maximum and minimum.

The relative maximum value of the function is approximately 4.012 when the x-value is −0.119

The relative minimum value is 1.558 with an x-value of 2.786

Look at the graph: it is rising from the left and stops at the relative maximum.

From this point the graph decreases until it reaches the relative minimum, and then it begins to rise again.

The function is increasing on the intervals:
$$(-\infty, -0.119) \text{ and } (1.558, \infty)$$

and decreasing on the interval:
$$(-0.119, 1.558).$$

Example 4:
Given $f(x) = 3x - 4$ and $g(x) = x^2 - 2x + 6$.

> We found $(f \circ g)(5) = 59$
>
> $(g \circ f)(5) = 105$

We will check these results using a graphing calculator:

1. On the equation screen we will enter: $Y_1 = 3x - 4$ for $f(x)$ and
$$Y_2 = x^2 - 2x + 6 \text{ for } g(x)$$

2. Then on the home screen use the VARS function to write $Y_1(Y_2(5))$ and $Y_2(Y_1(5))$.

> The results are 59 and 105.

Example 5:

Find if $x^2 + y^2 = 9$ is symmetric to the x-axis, the y-axis and the origin.

We will graph this equation in two parts:

$$Y_1 = \sqrt{9 - x^2}$$
$$Y_2 = -\sqrt{9 - x^2}$$

The graph is a circle with center at the origin and a radius of 3. Looking at the graph we see:

1. If the graph were folded on the x-axis, the parts of the graph above and below the axis are the same. Thus, there is symmetry on the x-axis.

2. If the graph were folded on the y-axis, the parts of the graph to the left and right of the axis are the same. Thus, there is symmetry on the y-axis.

3. If the graph is rotated $180°$, the resulting graph is the same as the original graph. Thus, there is symmetry around the origin.

Example 6:

Test $y = x^2 + 4$ for symmetry to the x-axis, the y-axis and the origin.

Use a graphing calculator to graph the equation:

$Y_1 = x^2 + 4$

Look at folding the graph to determine symmetry. If the graph were folded along the x-axis, the parts on either side of the axis do not coincide. The equation is not symmetric with respect to the x-axis.

If the graph were folded along the y-axis, the parts on the left and right of the axis would coincide so the graph is symmetric with respect to the y-axis

If the graph is rotated $180°$, the resulting graph is not the same as the original graph. Thus, there is no symmetry around the origin.

Example 7:

Are the given functions even, odd or neither?
    a. $f(x) = 2x^5 - x^3 + 4x$ b. $f(x) = 4x^4 + x^2$

a.   Graph setting $Y_1 = 2x^5 - x^3 + 4x$

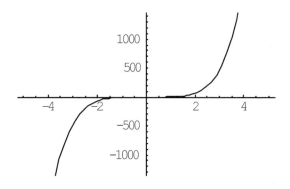

By looking at the graph, it appears that the function is symmetric with respect to the origin. Thus, the function is odd.

b. $f(x) = 4x^4 + x^2$

Graph by setting $Y_1 = 4x^4 + x^2$

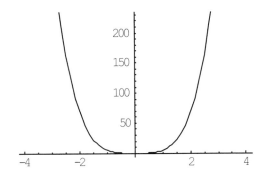

When looking at the graph, it appears that the function is symmetric with respect to the y-axis. Thus, the function is even.

Example 8.
For each , describe how the graph can be obtained from one of the basic graphs of x^2, x^3, and $|x|$

a. $h(x) = x^2 - 4$ b. $h(x) = (x - 3)^2$

c. $h(x) = |x| + 2$ d. $h(x) = |x - 2|$

e. $h(x) = x^3 + 1$ f. $h(x) = (x - 3)^3$

Solution:
For each of these graph the basic function and then the translated function and compare the two graphs.

a. For $h(x) = x^2 - 4$,
   $Y_1 = x^2$ and $Y_2 = x^2 - 4$

   Two graphs are drawn. The first is the basic graph and the second is the translated graph. The translation is   down 3 units

b. $h(x) = (x - 3)^2$:   Use $Y_1 = x^2$ and $Y_2 = (x - 3)^2$ right 3 units

c. $h(x) = |x| + 2$:   Use $Y_1 = |x|$ and $Y_2 = |x| + 2$ up 2 units

d. $h(x) = |x - 2|$:   Use $Y_1 = |x|$ and $Y_2 = |x - 2|$ right 2 units

e. $h(x) = x^3 + 1$:   Use $Y_1 = x^3$ and $Y_2 = x^3 + 1$ up 1 unit

f. $h(x) = (x - 3)^3$ Use $Y_1 = x^3$ and $Y_2 = (x - 3)^3$ right 3 units

Example 9.

Solve $4x - 3 = 2$

Solution:

Use a graphing calculator to graph each side of this equation and then use the **INTERSECT** feature to find the solution:

Graph by setting

$$Y_1 = 4x - 3 \quad \text{and} \quad Y_2 = 2$$

Use the **INTERSECT** feature to find where the two graphs intersect.

The x-value of the intersection point is the solution to the equation. We find this value to be 1.25.

If the solution is a rational number, we can change the answer to fraction form instead of decimal form by using the **FRAC▶**. The solution as a fraction is 5/4.

Example 10:

Solve: $2(4 - 2x) = 5 - 3(x + 1)$

Solution: Use the INTERSECT feature on a graphing calculator to find the solution of this equation.

Graph by setting $Y_1 = 2(4 - 2x) \quad \text{and} \quad Y_2 = 5 - 3(x + 1)$

Use the **INTERSECT** feature to find where the two graphs intersect. The x-value of the intersection point is the solution to the equation. We find this value to be 6.

Example 11:

Find the zero of $f(x) = 6x - 3$

Solution: We can use the ZERO feature from the CALC menu to find the zero of

$$f(x) = 6x - 3$$

Set $Y_1 = 6x - 3$

Next, select the **CALC** menu and then choose the ZERO feature.

We will enter a left and right bound and the guess choice on the *x*-intercept to get the result.

$$x = .5 \quad y = 0 \quad \text{or} \quad (.5, 0)$$

The zero is the *x*-coordinate of the *x*-intercept   and is 0.5.

Example 12:
Add the given complex numbers and then simplify the result:

    a. $(7 + 4i) + (9 + 5i)$:

                Set the calculator to "*a* + *bi*" MODE, and then enter the complex numbers using the *i* key.

                $(7 + 4i) + (9 + 5i)$ The result is $(16 + 9i)$.

Example 13:
Multiply and simplify the following complex numbers:

    a. $(1 - 3i)(1 + 2i)$ b. $(4 - 2i)^2$

Solution:

Set calculator to   *a+bi* MODE. Enter the problem as:

    a. $(1 - 3i)(1 + 2i)$ the result is: $7 - i$

    b. $(4 - 2i)^2$ the result is: $12 - 16i$

Example 14:

Express in the form *a+bi*, where *a* and *b* are real numbers

$$\frac{2 - i}{3 - 4i}$$

315

Solution:

Set the calculator to $a+bi$ MODE, and then enter the problem as:

$$((2-i)/(3-4i))$$

the result is $\dfrac{2}{5}+\dfrac{1}{5}i$

Example 15.

Solve $x^2 - 3x + 2 = 0$

Solution:

The solutions of the equation $x^2 - 3x + 2 = 0$ are the zeros of the function $f(x) = x^2 - 3x + 2$.

They are also the first coordinates of the x-intercepts of the graph of $f(x) = x^2 - 3x + 2$.

Let $Y_1 = x^2 - 3x + 2$.

Use the ZERO option in the CALCULATE menu. The x-value of one zero is 2 which is one of the solutions. The x-value of the other zero is 1 which is the other solution.

Solutions are: 2, 1

Example 16.

Solve: $x^2 - 4x + 1 = 0$

Solution:

Using the ZERO feature set $Y_1 = x^2 - 4x + 1$.

Use left bound, right bound and guess options to find the solutions.

The x-values of the zeros are the solutions, and

$x =$ 0.2679 and 3.7321

Example 17.

Solve $\dfrac{1}{2} - \dfrac{x-2}{3} = \dfrac{1}{6}$

Solution:

Set Y_1 equal to the left side of the equation, and

Y_2 equal to the right side of the equation.

Then select CALC option and choose INTERSECT.

The x-coordinate of the point of intersection of the two graphs is the solution to the equation.

The solution is: 3

Example 18.

For the equation, $\dfrac{1}{x} + \dfrac{1}{x-3} = \dfrac{x-2}{x-3}$, check the solutions of 3 and 1.

Solution:

Set Y_1 equal to the left side of the equation, and

Y_2 equal to the right side of the equation.

Use the TABLE method;   If $x = 1$, then $Y_1 = 0.5$ and $Y_2 = 0.5$.

If $x = 3$, then $Y_1 =$ ERROR and $Y_2 =$ ERROR

Thus 1 is a solution but 3 is not.

Example 19.

Solve $|x + 1| + 4 = 7$

Solution: Set $Y_1 = |x + 1| + 4$

$Y_2 = 7$

Use the CALC menu and select INTERSECT.

Find the first coordinates of the points of intersection.

The solutions are 2 and -4 .

Example 20.

Solve: $2x - 4 < 6 + 3x$

Solution: Set $Y_1 = 2x - 4$

$Y_2 = 6 + 3x$

Then use the GRAPH key.

The graph shows that for x values where $x < 2$, the graph of Y_1 lies below the graph of Y_2.

Therefore, on the interval $(-\infty, -2)$ we see from the graphs that $Y_1 < Y_2$.

Example 21.

Find the zeros of : $f(x) = x^3 - 2x^2 - 4x + 8$ and describe the graph at
the zeros

Solution: Set $Y_1 = x^3 - 2x^2 - 4x + 8$

Then use the Graph key to see the graph.

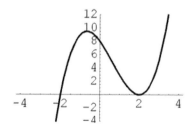

318

The graph shows that zeros occur at the x-values of − 2 and 2.

Notice that the graph at the zero of − 2 crosses the axis, and thus this zero of − 2 has an odd multiplicity.

At the zero of 2 the graph is tangent to the axis, and thus this zero has an even multiplicity.

Example 22.

$$f(x) = 0.5x^3 - 0.9x^2 - 0.8x + 1. \quad \text{Find the zeros of } f(x).$$

Solution: Set $Y_1 = 0.5x^3 - 0.9x^2 - 0.8x + 1.$

We will graph the function and use the ZERO feature to find the zeros of the function:

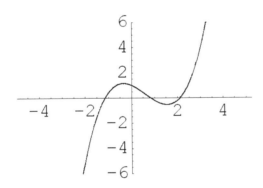

Select the CALC menu and select the ZERO feature.

The three zeros seen on the graph are:

$$x = -1.179, \ 0.831, \ \text{and} \ 2.105$$

Example 23.

      Given $f(x) = 3x^4 - 5x^3 - 2x^2 + x - 4$,   find $f(6)$.

Solution:

      Set $Y_1 = 3x^4 - 5x^3 - 2x^2 + x - 4$.

Use the VARS menu to locate the Y-Vars option.

Select Function, then select Y_1 and then Y_1 will be found on the home screen.

Enter (6)   and the home screen will have: $Y_1(6)$

Press enter. The answer will be on the home screen:

          The result is: 2738

Example 24.

      Given $f(x) = 6x^3 + 19x^2 + 2x - 3$. Find the factors of $f(x)$ and then solve the equation $f(x) = 0$.

Solution: Let $Y_1 = 6x^3 + 19x^2 + 2x - 3$

We will graph the function and use the ZERO feature to find the zeros of the function:

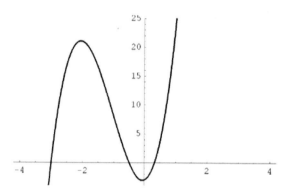

Select the CALC menu and use the ZERO feature.

The three zeros seen on the graph are:

      $-3,\ -1/2,\ 1/3$

320

Example 25.

Given $f(x) = 2x^5 - 2x^4 - 8x^3 + 8x^2 - 24x + 24$

    a. Find the rational zeros and then the other zeros; thus solve $f(x) = 0$.

    b. Factor $f(x)$ into linear factors.

Solution:

    a. Because the degree of $f(x)$ is 5, there are at most 5 distinct zeros. Using the Rational Zeros theorem, any rational zero of f must be of the form p/q,

p is any factor of 15   and q is any factor of 2.

The possibilities are:

Possibilities for p	$\pm 1, \pm 3, \pm 5, \pm 15$
Possibilities for q	$\pm 1, \pm 2$

Possibilities for p/q :

$1, -1, 3, -3, 5, -5, 15, -15, 1/2, -1/2, 3/2, -3/2,$
$5/2, -5/2, 15/2, -15/2$

Rather than using synthetic division to check each of these possibilities, we can graph the function:

Set $Y_1 = 2x^5 - 2x^4 - 8x^3 + 8x^2 - 24x + 24$

Graph:

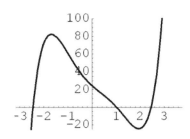

Look for zeros that appear to be near any of the possible rational zeros.

We see that $-5/2$, 1 and $5/2$ are possibilities:

Use synthetic division to check these three possibilities:

$$
\begin{array}{r|rrrrrr}
\underline{1}\ | & 2 & -2 & -8 & 8 & -24 & 24 \\
& & 2 & 0 & -8 & 0 & -24 \\
\hline
& 2 & 0 & -8 & 0 & -24 & 0
\end{array}
$$

Thus $x-1$ is a factor. So:

$$f(x) = (x-1)(2x^4 - 8x^2 - 24)$$

$$f(x) = (x-1)*2*(x^4 - 4x^2 - 12)$$

$$f(x) = (x-1)*2*(x^2 - 6)(x^2 + 2)$$

Now set the factors equal to zero and solve

$$x - 1 = 0 \qquad x^2 - 6 = 0 \qquad x^2 + 2 = 0$$

$$x = 1 \qquad\qquad x^2 = 6 \qquad\qquad x^2 = -2$$

$$x = 1 \qquad\qquad x = \pm\sqrt{6} \qquad x = \pm\sqrt{2}i$$

There is only one rational zero which is 1.

The other zeros are irrational/ imaginary.

b. The factorization into linear factors is:

$$f(x) = 2(x-1)(x+\sqrt{6})(x-\sqrt{6})(x+\sqrt{2}i)(x-\sqrt{2}i)$$

Example 26.

Given: $f(x) = \dfrac{1}{x-4}$

Find the domain and draw the graph.

322

Solution:

Set   Let $Y_1 = \dfrac{1}{x-4}$

The graph will be shown and the domain can be seen.

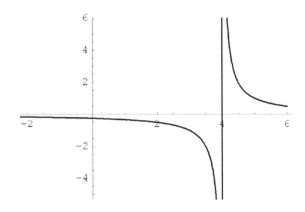

The vertical line seen in the graph is a vertical asymptote, and the graph does not cross that line.

The domain does not include the value $x = 4$:

Domain: $(-\infty, 4) \cup (4, \infty)$

Using DOT Mode, the vertical asymptote is not seen, and the graph is easier to read.

Example 27.

Solve: $x^3 - 4x > 0$

Solution:

We first find the zeros of the function $f(x) = x^3 - 4x$:

Set $Y_1 = x^3 - 4x$

Then find the zeros using ZERO under the CALC menu.

The zeros are $-2, 0, 2$.

323

Option 1. The intervals that result with these zeros are:

$$(-\infty,-2), \qquad (-2,0), \qquad (0,2), \qquad \text{and} \quad (2,\infty)$$

We can use the TABLE feature in the ASK mode to find the sign within each interval.

Option 2. We can determine the sign of $f(x)$ in each interval by looking at the graph of the function.

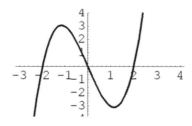

The graph is positive in the intervals:

$$(-2,0)\cup(2,\infty)$$

Example 28.
    Solve: $2x^4 - 3x^3 - 5x^2 \leq -x - 1$

Solution:

First, use addition/subtraction so that the right side of the inequality equal to zero.

Then graph: Set $Y_1 = 2x^4 - 3x^3 - 5x^2 + x + 1 = 0$

Graph the function and use the ZERO feature from the CALC menu to find the zeros:

324

The zeros are: -1, $-.414\,or\,(1-\sqrt{2})$, $1/2$, $2.414\,or\,1+\sqrt{2}$

These zeros define the intervals which need to be studied.

Looking at the graph we find the function graph is below the x-axis at:

$$(-1, 1-\sqrt{2}) \cup (1/2, 1+\sqrt{2})$$

Example 29.

Solve $\dfrac{x-2}{x+2} \geq \dfrac{x+3}{x-1}$

Solution:

Graph: Set $Y_1 = \dfrac{x-2}{x+2} - \dfrac{x+3}{x-1}$

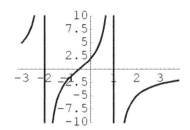

Use the ZERO feature to find the zero.

The zero is -0.5

By looking at the denominators we find that the domain cannot contain -2 and 1

The critical values are: -2, -0.5, and 1.

The graph shows where y is positive and where it is negative. Notice that -0.5 should be included in the solution since the inequality symbol is $\geq$ and it is also a zero.

The solution set is: $(-\infty, -2) \cup [-1/2, 1)$

Example 30.

Which of the following are one-to-one functions?

a. $f(x) = 6 - 2x$ 	 b. $f(x) = x^2 + 3$

c. $f(x) = x^3 - 3x$

Solution:

a. Let $Y_1 = 6 - 2x$ and graph:

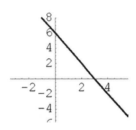

One-to-one because no horizontal line intersects the graph more than once.

b. Set $Y_1 = x^2 + 3$ and graph

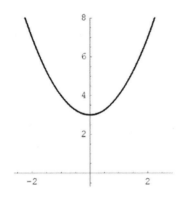

Not one-to-one since there are many horizontal lines that intersect the graph more than once.

c. Let $Y_1 = x^3 - 3x$

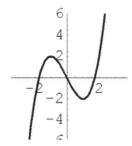

Not one-to-one since there are many horizontal lines that intersect the graph more than once.

Example 31.

If P dollars is deposited into an account paying a rate of interest r compounded n times, then after t years the account will contain:

$$A = P\left(1 + \frac{r}{n}\right)^{nt}$$

If $10,000 is deposited at 10% interest, compounded quarterly, how many years must the money be deposited in order for the amount to reach $25,000? Define a function of time with the given money, and interest, and then use the amount of money in the account to solve for t.

Solution: Use the given information to set up the exponential equation:

$$25,000 = 10,000\left(1 + \frac{0.10}{4}\right)^{4t}$$

Let $Y_1 = 25,000$

Let $Y_2 = 10,000(1.025)^{4x}$

Graph both equations and then use INTERSECT to estimate the first coordinate of the point of intersection which is the x-value at that point.

For your window use x-min = 0, x-max = 30000, y-min = 0 and y-max = 30000.

The result is 2.264 years.

Example 32.

Find the following common logarithms on a calculator. If you are using a graphing calculator, be sure that you are in REAL mode.

a. log 45781   b. log 0.00003456   c. log(− 2)

Solution: Find the key on the calculator marked LOG. This is the key for the common logarithm. Use the LOG key with the numbers.

a. log 45781 = 4.66069

b. log 0.00003456 = − 4.48732

c. log(− 2) does not exist

These answers can be checked for correctness by raising 10 to the answers found and see that this indeed does equal the original number.

$$10^{4.66069} = 45781.49811$$

The slight difference from the original number 45781 is due to the rounding feature within the calculator.

Example 33.

With a calculator find each of the following.

a.   ln 45781   b. ln 0.00003456   c. ln (− 2)

.   d.   ln 1   e. ln 0

Solution: Find the key on the calculator marked LN. This is the key for the natural logarithm. Use the LN key with the numbers. Be sure to use the REAL Mode.

a.   ln 45781 = 10.73162

b.   ln 0.00003456 = 10.27281

c.   ln (− 2) = does not exist

d.   ln 1 = 0

e.   ln 0 = does not exist

These answers can be checked for correctness by raising e to the answers found and see that this indeed does equal the original number.

Example 34.   Graph $y = f(x) = \log_6 x$

Solution: First change the base to either base 10 or base e

$$y = \log_6 x = \frac{\log x}{\log 6}$$

Set $Y_1 = \dfrac{\log x}{\log 6}$ and then graph.

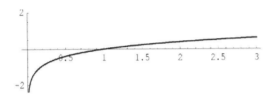

Example 35.

Solve: $\ln x - \ln(x+1) = 3\ln 4$

Solution: The solution of the equation $\ln x - \ln(x+1) = 3\ln 4$ is the zero of the function:

$$f(x) = \ln x - \ln(x+1) - 3\ln 4$$

Let $Y_1 = \ln x - \ln(x+1) - 3\ln 4$

The solution will be the first coordinate of the x-intercept .

The graph is:

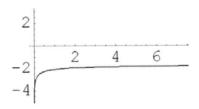

There is no x-intercept. The answer is: no solution

Example 36

Solve: $\log_2(x+7) + \log_2 x = 3$

Solution: We must use the change of base formula and graph the equation.

Let $Y_1 = \dfrac{\log(x+7)}{\log 2} + \dfrac{\log x}{\log 2}$ Let $Y_2 = 3$

Graph the equations and use the Intersect Mode to find the solution

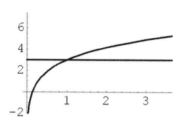

The solution is $x = 1$.

Example 37.

Solve: $\log_4 x = -1$

Solution: Use the change-of-base formula and graph the equations.

Let $Y_1 = \dfrac{\log x}{\log 4}$ Let $Y_2 = -1$

Graph and use the Intersect Mode to find the solution. The first coordinate of the point of intersection is the solution:

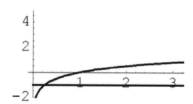

The solution is $x = 1/4$.

Solve: $\log_3(x+3) + \log_3(x+5) = 1$

Solution: Use the change-of-base formula and graph the equations.

Let $Y_1 = \dfrac{\log(x+3)}{\log 3} + \dfrac{\log(x+5)}{\log 3}$ Let $Y_2 = 1$

Graph and use the INTERSECT Mode to find the solution. The first coordinate of the point of intersection is the solution.

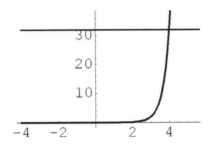

The solution is $x = -2$

Example 39.

Solve: $2^{4x-11} = 32$

Solution:

Let $Y_1 = 2^{4x-11}$ Let $Y_2 = 32$

Graph and use the INTERSECT Mode to find the first coordinate of the point of intersection.

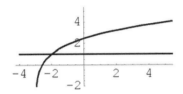

The solution is $x = 4$

Example 40.

Solve: $3^x = 22$

Solution:

Set $Y_1 = 3^x$ Set $Y_2 = 22$

Graph and use the INTERSECT Mode to find the first coordinate of the point of intersection.

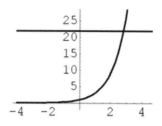

The solution is approximately 2.81359

Example 41.

Solve: $2 = e^{0.4t}$

Solution:

Let $Y_1 = e^{0.4x}$ Let $Y_2 = 2$

Graph and use the INTERSECT Mode to find the first coordinate of the point of intersection.

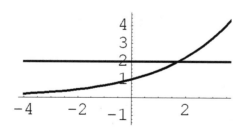

The solution is approximately 1.73286795

Example 42.

Solve $e^x + e^{-x} - 8 = 0$

Solution: We will graph the equation and use the ZERO method.

Let $Y_1 = e^x + e^{-x} - 8$

Graph, then find the zeros.

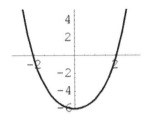

The zeros are approximately: -2.0634 and 2.0634

Example 43.

Suppose $10,000 is invested at an interest rate of r, compounded continuously, and grows to $14,190.68 in 5 years.

Find the interest rate.

Solution: Use the continuously compounded interest formula

$$A = Pe^{rt}$$

Substitute in the values

$$14,190.68 = 10,000\,e^{5r} \quad \text{or} \quad 1.419068 = e^{5r}$$

We will use the INTERSECT mode to solve this equation

Set $Y_1 = e^{5r}$ and Set $Y_2 = 1.419068$

Graph. The first coordinate of the point of intersection will be the value of r

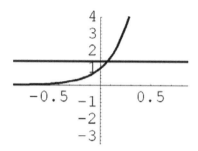

The intersection point $x = .07000006$ $y = 14190.68$

The interest rate is the x-value and is 0.07 which is 7%

Example 44.
   Solve the given system of equations:

$$3x + 4y = 5$$
$$2x + 3y = 4$$

Solution: Before we can enter either equation into the calculator, we must solve each equation for y.

$$3x + 4y = 5$$
$$2x + 3y = 4$$
becomes
$$y = 1/4(-3x + 5)$$
$$y = 1/3(-2x + 4)$$

Let $Y_1 = 1/4(-3x + 5)$ and   let $Y_2 = 1/3(-2x + 4)$

Graph the two equations and use the INTERSECT Mode.

The solution is the intersection point of the two equations and is $(-1, 2)$

By looking at the graph, we cannot determine the solution.

Because we are able to use the INTERSECT Mode, we can find the solution.

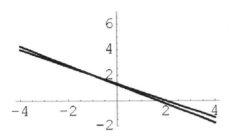

Example 45.

John wants to invest $30,000. With part of his money he buys shares in a mutual fund, paying 9% per year. He invests the rest of the money in municipal bonds paying 10% per year. After the first year he earns interest of $2820. How much is invested at each rate?

Solution: Write a system of equations to solve this problem.

Let

x = the amount of money invested at 9%

y = the amount of money invested at 10%

We will write the first equation about the total money invested.

$$x + y = 30000$$

The second equation will calculate the interest earned in 1 year.

$$0.09x + 0.10y = 2820$$

Our system is:

$$x + y = 30000$$
$$0.09x + 0.10y = 2820$$

Solving each of these for y we get:

$$y = 30000 - x$$
$$y = 1/9(282000 - 9x)$$

Set $Y_1 = 30000 - x$ and   Set $Y_2 = 1/9(282000 - 9x)$

335

Graph the two equations and use the INTERSECT Mode.

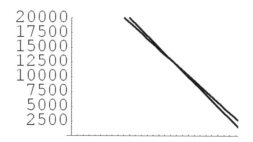

Using the calculator we can locate the point of intersection.

$18,000 is invested at 9% and $12,000 is invested at 10%.

Example 46.

Six hundred tickets were sold for a school play. The price of tickets for adults was $3.00 and for children was $1.00. If the sale of tickets resulted in a total of $1400, how many tickets of each kind were sold?

Solution: We will write a system of equations to solve this problem.

Let

x = the number of adult tickets sold

y = the number of child tickets sold

We will write the first equation about the total number of the tickets..

$$x + y = 600$$

The second equation will be about the money.

$$3.00x + 1.00y = 1400$$

Our system is:
$$x + y = 600$$
$$3x + 1y = 1400$$

We must first solve each equation for y

$$y = 600 - x$$

$$y = 1400 - 3x$$

Set $Y_1 = 600 - x$ and   Set $Y_2 = 1400 - 3x$

Graph the two equations and use the INTERSECT Mode.

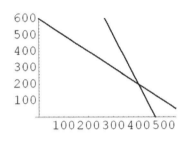

Finding the point of intersection, we get the solution:

400 adult tickets and 200 child tickets were sold.

Example 47.

Graph: $2x + y \le 6$

Solution: To graph this inequality on a graphing calculator, we first enter the related equation in the form:

$$y = -2x + 6 \quad \text{(solve for } y\text{)}$$

Let $Y_1 = -2x + 6$.

Then select the "shade below" the graph style.

337

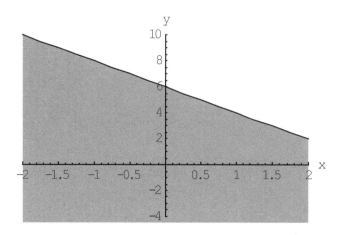

Example 48. Graph:
$$x + 2y \le 6$$
$$x - y \ge 3$$

Solution: First we must convert each inequality to an equation.

$$x + 2y = 6 \qquad \text{and} \qquad x - y = 3$$

Then solve each for y

$$y = \frac{6 - x}{2} \qquad \text{and} \qquad y = x - 3$$

$$\text{Set} \quad Y_1 = \frac{6 - x}{2} \qquad \text{and} \qquad Y_2 = x - 3$$

Use different shading patterns on a graphing calculator to graph the system of inequalities. The solution set is the region shaded using both patterns.

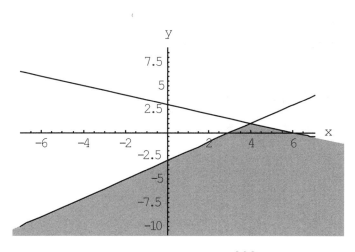

338

Example 49.

Find the product of the two given matrices:

$$A = \begin{bmatrix} 1 & 3 & -4 \\ 4 & 0 & -2 \end{bmatrix} \quad \text{and} \quad B = \begin{bmatrix} 5 & -4 & 2 & 0 \\ -1 & 6 & 3 & 1 \\ 7 & 0 & 5 & 8 \end{bmatrix}$$

Solution: To multiply matrices on a graphing calculator, first we enter each matrix.

Use the MATRIX mode to edit the matrix and enter the appropriate elements:

After the matrices are entered, use matrix operations on the home screen.

Again, use the MATRIX mode to enter the first matrix name on the home screen and then enter the second matrix name:

$$[A][B]$$

The solution to the matrix multiplication will appear on the screen.

$$AB = \begin{bmatrix} -26 & 14 & -9 & -29 \\ 6 & -16 & -2 & -16 \end{bmatrix}$$

Example 50. Find the inverse of the matrix A.

$$A = \begin{bmatrix} 2 & 4 \\ 1 & 5 \end{bmatrix}$$

Solution: Enter the given matrix and then take the inverse.

First, using MATRIX Mode, enter the given matrix as a 2 X 2 matrix A.

Return to the home screen and enter the matrix entered:

$$[A]$$

Then use the reciprocal key:

$$[A]^{-1}$$

339

The computer screen shows the solution matrix.

$$A^{-1} = \begin{bmatrix} 5/6 & -2/3 \\ -1/6 & 1/3 \end{bmatrix}$$

Example 51.

Solve the following system of equations:

$$x - y + z = 4$$
$$2x + y + 3z = 7$$
$$-x - 4y - z = 1$$

Solution:

We will write the system in matrix form and then use the fact that:

$$X = A^{-1}C$$

Use MATRIX mode to enter

$$A = \begin{bmatrix} 1 & -1 & 1 \\ 2 & 1 & 3 \\ -1 & -4 & -1 \end{bmatrix} \quad \text{and} \quad C = \begin{bmatrix} 4 \\ 7 \\ 1 \end{bmatrix}$$

On the home screen enter the matrix names and the inverse key for A:

$$[A]^{-1}[C]$$

The result is the matrix showing the solution: $(1, -1, 2)$.

Thus, $x = 1$, $y = -1$, and $z = 2$

Example 52. If $B = \begin{bmatrix} -2 & 4 \\ 6 & 8 \end{bmatrix}$ find $\delta(B)$ which is the determinant of matrix B.

Solution: Begin by entering the matrix B in the calculator using MATRIX mode.

Then use the MATRIX MATH menu and select : det(

Enter the name of the matrix and select the Enter key.

$$\det\left([B]\right) = -40$$

Example 53.

Given matrix A. Find the determinant of A.

$$A = \begin{bmatrix} -1 & 3 & 2 \\ 1 & 4 & 0 \\ 3 & -2 & 5 \end{bmatrix}$$

Solution: Begin by entering the matrix into the calculator using MATRIX mode.

Then use the MATRIX MATH menu and select : det(

Enter the name of the matrix and select the Enter key.

$$\det\left([A]\right) = 63$$

Geometry-Algebra Review

Triangle

  Pythagorean Theorem: $a^2 + b^2 = c^2$

  Area: $A = 1/2\,bh$

Square

  Area: $A = s^2$ **Perimeter:** $P = 4s$

Rectangle

  Area: $A = LW$ **Perimeter:** $P = 2L + 2W$

Parallelogram

  Area: $A = bh$

Rhombus

  Perimeter: $P = 4a$

Circle $(x - h)^2 + (y - k)^2 = r^2$

  Area: $A = \pi r^2$ **Circumference:** $C = 2\pi r$ **or** $C = \pi d$

  Diameter: $D = 2r$

Midpoint $\left(\dfrac{x_1 + x_2}{2}, \dfrac{y_1 + y_2}{2} \right)$

Distance Formula: $d = \sqrt{(x_1 - x_2)^2 + (y_1 - y_2)^2}$

Variation

  Direct: $y = kx\ (k \neq 0)$

  Inverse: $y = \dfrac{k}{x}\ (k \neq 0)$

  Joint: $y = kxz\ (k \neq 0)$

Interval Notation

  $(a, b) = \{ x \mid a < x < b \}$

  $[a, \infty) = \{ x \mid x \geq a \}$

Equation Solving

  if $a = b \Rightarrow a + c = b + c$

  if $a = b \Rightarrow ac = bc$

  if $x^2 = k \Rightarrow x = \sqrt{k}$ or $x = -\sqrt{k}$

Subsets of Real Numbers

Natural numbers = $\{1, 2, 3, \ldots\}$
Whole numbers = $\{0, 1, 2, 3, \ldots\}$
Integers = $\{\ldots, -3, -2, -1, 0, 1, 2, 3, \ldots\}$

Rational = $\{\frac{a}{b} \mid a$ and b are integers with $b \neq 0\}$

Irrational = $\{x \mid x$ is not rational$\}$

Properties of Real Numbers
(with real numbers a, b, and c)
Commutative: $a + b = b + a$; $a * b = b * a$
Associative: $(a + b) + c = a + (b + c)$; $(ab)c = a(bc)$
Distributive: $a(b + c) = ab + ac$; $a(b - c) = ab - ac$
Identity: $a + 0 = a$; $a * 1 = a$
Inverse: $a + (-a) = 0$; $\frac{1}{a} * a = 1 \ (a \neq 0)$
Multiplication property of zero: $a * 0 = 0$

Absolute Value

$$|a| = \begin{cases} a & \text{for } a \geq 0 \\ -a & \text{for } a < 0 \end{cases}$$

Order of Operations
1. Evaluate within group symbols
2. Exponential expressions
3. Multiplication and division
4. Addition and subtraction

Exponent Rules

$a^{p+r} = a^p * a^r$ $\qquad$ $\dfrac{a^p}{a^r} = a^{p-r}$

$(a^p)^r = a^{pr}$ $\qquad$ $(ab)^r = a^r b^r$

$a^{-r} = \dfrac{1}{a^r}$ $\qquad$ $\dfrac{1}{a^{-r}} = a^r$

$\left(\dfrac{a}{b}\right)^r = \dfrac{a^r}{b^r}$ $\qquad$ $\left(\dfrac{a}{b}\right)^{-r} = \left(\dfrac{b}{a}\right)^r$

$a^0 = 1$ $\qquad$ $a^{-1} = \dfrac{1}{a}$

Roots and Radicals

$$a^{1/n} = \sqrt[n]{a}$$

$$a^{m/n} = (\sqrt[n]{a})^m = \sqrt[n]{a^m}$$

$$\sqrt[n]{ab} = \sqrt[n]{a} * \sqrt[n]{b}$$

$$\sqrt[n]{\frac{a}{b}} = \frac{\sqrt[n]{a}}{\sqrt[n]{b}}$$

Factoring

$$a^2 + 2ab + b^2 = (a+b)^2$$

$$a^2 - 2ab + b^2 = (a-b)^2$$

$$a^2 - b^2 = (a+b)(a-b)$$

$$a^3 - b^3 = (a-b)(a^2 + ab + b^2)$$

$$a^3 + b^3 = (a+b)(a^2 - ab + b^2)$$

Rational Expressions

$$\frac{a}{b} + \frac{c}{b} = \frac{a+c}{b}$$

$$\frac{a}{b} - \frac{c}{b} = \frac{a-c}{b}$$

$$\frac{ac}{bc} = \frac{a}{b}$$

$$\frac{a}{b} + \frac{c}{d} = \frac{ad+bc}{bd}$$

$$\frac{a}{b} * \frac{c}{d} = \frac{ac}{bd}$$

$$\frac{a}{b} \div \frac{c}{d} = \frac{a}{b} * \frac{d}{c}$$

If $\frac{a}{b} = \frac{c}{d}$ then $ad = bc$.

Exercise Answers

Exercises 1.1
1. Yes   3. Yes   5. Yes. 7. Yes. 9. Yes 11. Yes 13. $-2, 0, 3$ 15. $0, 2, 4$
17. $0, -2, 40, 9m^2+9m$ 19. $0, -2$, Undefined, $-7/2$ 21. $4, 5, 2, 2$ 23. $10, -5$,
$8m^2+6m^2-4$ 25. All real numbers   27. All real numbers 29. $x \neq 3$. 31. All Real
numbers 33. All real numbers; 35. $[=2,0)U(0,\infty)$; 37 All real numbers.

Exercises 1.2
1. 0;   3. no slope;   5. 1/4;   7. 1/7;   9. 8/3;   11. 9/4;   13. 0;   15. 4;   17. no slope;
19. 1.625;   21. 3;   23. no slope; 25. 2; 27. 1/3; 29. 0; 31. 2.

Exercises 1.3
1. $2/5$; $(0, -5)$; 3. 0, $(0, 3/4)$; 5. $-1/2$, $(0, 7)$; 7. $-2/3$, $(0, 4)$;   9. 0, $(0, 3)$;
11. $4/5$, $(0, 12/5)$;   21; $y = 4x + 3$;   23. $y = -3x + 4$;   25. $y = -3.5x - 2$;
27. $y = -\dfrac{2}{3}x + \dfrac{17}{3}$;   29. $y = -3x - 3$; 31. $y = 2/3x + 11/3$; 33. $y = -3/7x + 25/7$;
35. $y = -x + 5$; 37. $y = -2$, $x = 0$; 39. $y = 2$, $x = 1$;   41. neither;   43. neither;
45. perpendicular   47. $y = 2x + 6$, $y = -1/2x + 7/2$; 49. $y = -1/2x - 1/2$; $y = 2x + 5$;
51. $x = 3$, $y = 1$;   53. true; 55. false.

Exercises 1.4
1. increasing $(0,\infty)$; decreasing $(-\infty,0)$. Relative minimum $(0,0)$
3. increasing $(0,\infty)$, decreasing $(-\infty,0)$. Relative minimum $(0, -3)$
5. constant $(-\infty,\infty)$.   7. increasing $(-\infty,\infty)$. ;
9. increasing $(0,\infty)$; decreasing $(-\infty,0)$. Relative minimum $(0, 2)$
11. $A(x) = x(50 - x)$ or $A(x) = 50x - x^2$
13. $h(d) = \sqrt{d^2 - 5000}$
15. $A(w) = w(200 - w)$ or $A(w) = 200w - w^2$.

Exercises 1.5
1. 51;   3. 1/2; 5. $\dfrac{4}{4\sqrt{2}+3}$;   7. 22;   9. $-8/5$;

11. $x+2$, $5x - 6$, $8x^3 + 6x^2$; $9x^2 - 12x + 4$; $\dfrac{3x-2}{4-2x}$, $16 - 16x + 4x^2$; $\dfrac{4-2x}{3x-2}$

13. $\sqrt{x+1} + x - 2$; $\sqrt{x+1} - x + 2$; $x\sqrt{x+1} - 2\sqrt{x+1}$; $x+1$; $\dfrac{\sqrt{x+1}}{x-2}$; $x^2 - 4x + 4$;

$\dfrac{x-2}{\sqrt{x+1}}$;   15. $|x| + x - 2$; $|x| - x + 2$; $x|x| - 2|x|$; $|x^2|$; $\dfrac{|x|}{x-2}$; $x^2 - 4x + 4$

347

$\dfrac{x-2}{|x|}$; 17. $4x+2h$; 19. $6x-4+3h$; 21. -1; 23. -1; 25. $x+2$, all real numbers,.

$x+2$, all real numbers; 27. $f(x)=x^3, g(x)=7-x$; 29 $f(x)=x^2, g(x)=\sqrt{x}-4$

Exercises 1.6:
5. y-axis; 7. neither; 9. y-axis; 11. y-axis; 13. origin; 15.$(1/2, 0), (-1/2,0), (-1/2, 0)$;
17. $(2, -1/3),(-2, 1/3),(-2, -1/3)$; 19. $(5, 4), (-5, -4), (-5, 4)$;
21. odd; 23. even; 25. odd; 27. neither; 29. reflected across x-axis; 31. left 2;
33. shrunk by 1/3; 35. shifted right 4 and down 3.

Chapter 1 Review:
1. no; domain $\{2, 4, 6\}$; range $\{3, 5, 7\}$ 2. no, domain $\{2\}$; range $\{4, 5, 6, 7\}$
3. yes

4. yes

5. yes

6. all real numbers

7. $(-\infty, 0) \cup (0, \infty)$

8. $(-\infty, -2) \cup (-2, 3) \cup (3, \infty)$

9. $(-\infty, \infty)$

10. 1

11. 9

12. y^2+2y+1

13. 1

14. 1

15. 0

16. no slope

17. 1/11

18. $-3/2$; $(0, -9/2)$

19. $y=-4x+3$

20. $y=-1/3x+4$

21. $y=-2/3x-5/3$

22. parallel

23. parallel

24. $y=2x-2$

25. $y=-1/2x-3$

26. $y=-2$

27. $x=1$

28. $\sqrt{x+2}=x^2-2$

29. 0

30. 3

31. x^2-5x+9; x^2+x-3

32. all

33. all

34. none

35. y-axis

36. origin

37. y-axis

38. y-axis

39. none

40. $y=(x+3)^2-4$

41. $y=|1/3x|+2$

42. $y=-\sqrt{x+2}-4$

Exercises 2.1:
1. 7; 3. 7/2; 5. -2; 7. 7; 9. 3; 11. 5; 13. -4; 15. -3; 17. 5; 19. 7/3;
21. $2A/b$ 23. $y-mx$; 25. $(P-2W)2$; 27. $T/(pc+e)$; 29. $(6-3y)/2$;
31. $t/(1-w)$

Exercises 2.2:
1. $10+5i$; 3. $1+2i$; 5. $-6-2i$; 7. $5-2i$; 9. $6+8i$; 11. $-1-i$; 13. $8+6i$;
15. $8+24i$; 17. $-10+11i$; 19. $-18-26i$; 21. $7+17i$; 23. $38+9i$; 25. $5+12i$;

27. $\dfrac{4}{13} - \dfrac{19}{13}i$;   29 i;   31. $-i$;   33. 1.

Exercises 2.3:

1. $-4, 5$;   3. $-1, 1/2$;   5. 0, 4;   7. $-2, 2$; 9. $\pm\dfrac{\sqrt{26}}{2}$;   11. $\pm i\sqrt{2}$;   13. $\pm\sqrt{11}$;

15. $\pm\sqrt{2}$;   17. $-2, 0, 1/3$;   19. $-5, 1$;   21. $-4, -2$;   23. $-2, 9$;

25. $\dfrac{-3 \pm \sqrt{13}}{2}$;   27. 2 irrational roots;   29. 2 rational roots;   31. 1 rational.

Exercises 2.4:
1. $(2; -16)$, $x = 2$, min $= -16$;   3. $(4, -4)$, $x = 4$, min $= -4$;   5. $(-3/2, 21/4)$, $x = -3/2$, min $= 21/4$;   7. $(-2, 4)$, $x = -2$, max $= 4$;   9. $(-1/3, 4/3)$, $x = -1/3$, max $= 4/3$;   11. $(1, 3)$, $x = 1$, min $= 3$;   13. $(7/2, -25/4)$, min value $= -25/4$, range: $(-25/4, \infty)$, increasing: $(7/2, \infty)$, decreasing: $(-\infty, 7/2)$;   15. $(3/2, -1/2)$, max value: $-1/2$, range: $(-\infty, -1/2)$; increasing $(-\infty, 3/2)$, decreasing: $(3/2, \infty)$;   17 .9375sec, 18.0625 ft.

Exercises 2.5:
1. 12/5;   3. 4;   5. 4;   7. $-5, 2$;   9. $-3, 3$;   11. 2;   13. No solution.;   15. 1;   17. No solution;   19. 0, 1;   21. 3;   23. $-4, 4$;   25. $-9, 3$;   27. $-4, 10$;   29. $-4, 0$.

Exercise 2.6:
1. $x > 5$;   3. $x > 8/3$;   5. $x \geq -15/14$;   7. $[-5, 4)$;   9. $[1, 7)$;   11. $[2, 4)$;   13. $(-\infty, 5) \cup (12, \infty)$ 15. $(-\infty, -29/3) \cup (41/2, \infty)$;   17. $(-6, 6)$;   19. $(-9, 3)$;   21. $(-\infty, -16) \cup (2, \infty)$;   23. $(23/4, 25/4)$;   25. $[-7, 3]$;   27. $[-4, 5/3]$;   29. $(-\infty, -11] \cup [13, \infty)$.

Chapter 2 Review:
1. 1
2. -4
3. 7
4. $1/2, -2/3$
5. $2, -3$
6. $4/3, -2$
7. $\pm\sqrt{5}$
8. $\pm\sqrt{6}$
9. 4
10. 5
11. 1/3
12. -1
13. $-4, 6$
14. $-3, 1/2$
15. 0
16. -3
17. 1/2
18. 5
19. $-1, 7$
20. $-9, 6$
21. $[-5/2, 2]$
22. $(1, 5]$
23. $(-\infty, -2) \cup (2, \infty)$
24. $(-\infty, 1] \cup [5, \infty)$
25. $(-1/2, 1)$
26. $(-\infty, -8) \cup (-2, \infty)$

27. $\dfrac{V}{lw}$　　　　　　　28. $\dfrac{v^2}{3p}$

29. $-2i\sqrt{5}$　　　　　　30. $-6\sqrt{2}$

31. $-3/4$　　　　　　　　32. -24

33. $18+14i$　　　　　　　34. $2+i$

35. $8/5+1/5i$　　　　　36. $4/5-3/5i$

37. $-2/3,\ 4,\ -3$　　　　38. $2\pm i\sqrt{6}$

39. $-3,6$　　　　　　　　40. $\pm\sqrt{2},\ \pm 1$

Exercises 3.1

1. quartic, $3x^4$, 3, 4;　3. linear, $0.3x$, 0.3, 1;　5. quadratic, $134\,x^2$, 134, 2;
7. cubic, $-3x^3$, -3, 3;　9. constant, -5, -5, zero;　11. ∞ to $-\infty$;
13. $-\infty$ to $-\infty$;　15. $-\infty$ to ∞;　17. 3, multiplicity 2, 4, multiplicity 1;
19. 2, multiplicity 3, -2, multiplicity 1;　21. 1, multiplicity 2, -5, multiplicity 3,
0, multiplicity 4.

Exercises 3.2

1. 6, 6, 5;　3. 3, 3, 2;　5. 5, 5, 4;　7. $\infty, \infty, -6$;　9. $-\infty, \infty, -2$;　11. $-\infty, \infty, 4$;
17. yes;　19. yes.

Exercises 3.3

1. no;　3. yes;　5. yes;　7. $x^2-2x+4, -35$;　9. $2x^2+x-3, -2$;　11. no;
13. yes;　15. $x^2+4x+16, 0$;　17. $x^2+4x+9, -13$;　19. -18;
21. $(x+1)(x+2)(x-2), -2, -2, 2$

Exercises 3.4

1. $x^3-7x^2+7x+15$;　3. x^3-4x^2+x-4;　5. x^3+2x^2-9x-4;　7. x^3-x^2-6x;
9. $x^5+4x^4+4x^3-4x^2-16x-16$;　11. $-\sqrt{3}$;　13. $-2i$;　15. $-\sqrt{3},\ 2i$;
17. $x^3-7x^2+17x-15$;　19. x^4+7x^2-18;　21. $\pm 1/2, \pm 1, \pm 2, \pm 4$;
23. $4, 2+\sqrt{3}, 2-\sqrt{3}$;　25. $-1, -2, -3, 4$

Exercises 3.5

1. vertical $x=4$, horizontal $y=0$;　3. vertical $x=2$, horizontal $y=1$;
5. vertical $x=3/5$, horizontal $y=4/5$;　7. vertical $x=2$, $x=-2$, horizontal $y=0$;
9. vertical $x=-1$, oblique $y=x-1$;　11. vertical $x=2$, $x=1/3$, horizontal $y=1$;
13. horizontal $y=2$;
15.

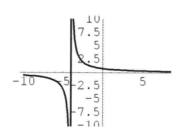

350

17.

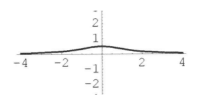

19.

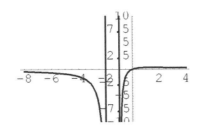

21. $f(x) = \dfrac{1}{x^2 - 9}$;   22. $f(x) = \dfrac{4(x^2 + 2x + 1)}{3(x + 2)(x - 3)}$

Exercises 3.6

1. $-6, 3$;   3. $-\infty, 1] \cup [2, \infty)$;   5. $(-6, 3)$;   7. $(-\infty, 1) \cup (2, \infty)$;

9. $(-\infty, -3) \cup (4, \infty)$;   11. $(-\infty, -6) \cup (6, \infty)$;   13. $(-4, -2)$;

15. $(-\infty, -\sqrt{5}] \cup [0, \sqrt{5})$ 17. $(-6, 3]$;   19. $(-3, -1)$

Chapter 3 Review

1. $-2, 2$; min 2; $(-\infty, \infty)$; $[-2, \infty)$;   2. $-2, 2$; min -2; $(-\infty, \infty)$; $(-\infty, \infty)$;

3. $-2\sqrt{2}, 0, \sqrt{2}$; min -16, max 0, $(-\infty, \infty)$; $[-16, \infty)$;   4. cubic; $-7x^3, -7, 3$;

5. quartic, $-37x^4$; -37; 4   7. constant, 4, 4, 0;   8. quadratic, $3x^2$; 3; 2;

9. as $x \to -\infty$, $f \to -\infty$; as $x \to \infty$, $f \to \infty$ 10. as $x \to -\infty$, $f \to -\infty$;

as $x \to \infty, f \to -\infty$;   11. 2, mult. 3, 0, mult. 1, -2, mult. 2

12. -3, mult. 1, -1, mult. 1, 1, mult. 1, 3, mult. 1;   13. -5, mult. 1, -3, mult.1,

5, mult. 1;   14. yes;   15. no;   16. $Q(x) = x^2 + 9x + 15$, $r = 79$;

17. $Q(x) = x^3 + 2x^2 + 4x + 8$; $r = 0$;   18. no, no;   19. yes, no;   20. 2, -2, $3i$, $-3i$;

21. -3, $-i, i$;   22. $f(x) = x^2 - 5$;   23. $f(x) = x^3 + 2x^2 + x + 2$;   24. $(-5, 5)$;

25. $(-\infty, 3) \cup (3, \infty)$;   26. $(-1, 3)$

Exercises 4.1

1. $\{(4,5), (3,-2), (7,4)\}$;   3. $x = 3y + 2$;   5. $x = 2y^2 - y$;   7. $y = x^2 + 7x$;

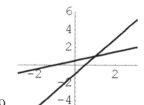 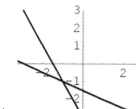

9.   11.

13. $f(a) = 4a - 3, f(b) = 4b - 3; 4a - 3 = 4b - 3; 4a = 4b; a = b.$ 15. $f(-1) = 3; f(1) = 3$

17. no;   19. yes;   21. no;   23. $f^{-1}(x) = \dfrac{1}{x}$;   25. $f^{-1}(x) = \sqrt{2-x}$

Exercises 4.2
1. e;   2. f.;   3. a;   4. b;   5. c ;   6. d;

7.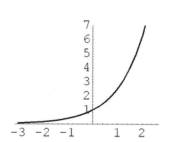

9.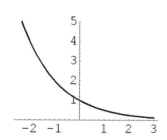

11.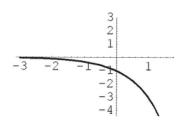

13.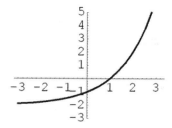

15.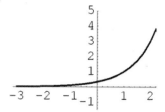

17.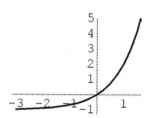

19.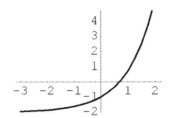

21.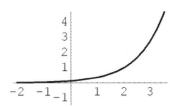

23.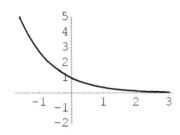

<u>Exercises 4.3</u>

1.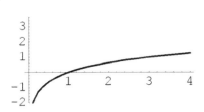

3.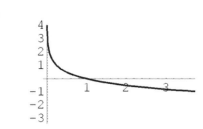

5.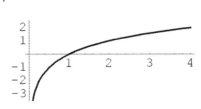

7.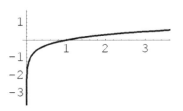

9. 8;   11. 2;   13. 0;   15. -2;   17. undefined;   19. 1;   21. 2;   23. 3;
25. 1/3;   27. 1/2;   29. $\log 10{,}000 = 4$;   31. $\log_m 4 = t$ 33. $10^{0.9031} = 8$;

35. $a^p = R$;   37 $\dfrac{\log 24}{\log 3}$;   39. 20.6070; 90.7928; 119.5182; 140.3743

<u>Exercises 4.4</u>

1. $\log_4 17 + \log_4 12$;   3. $\log_m 12 + \log_m T$;   5. $\ln 3 + \ln x$;   7. $\log_a m - \log_a n$;
9. $4\log_9 x$;   11. $-4\log_n T$;   13. $\log_7 5 + \log_7 r + 3\log_7 s + 6\log_r t$;

353

15. $4\log_b x - 5/2\log_b y - 3/2\log_b z$;   17. $\log_b 120$;   19. $\log_b \dfrac{\sqrt{x}(w^3)}{q^5}$;

21. 1.1461;   23. -0.5441.

Exercises 4.5
1. 3;   3. $\log 28/\log 3$;   5. 1/2;   7. 0;   9. $-\ln 0.06/0.4$;   11. $\ln 52/\ln 5.3$;
13. 262,144;   15. e^2;   17. 5;   19. 1;   21. $-1+\sqrt{3}$;   23. 9.

Exercises 4.6
1. $231 e^{(0.0103*45)} = 367.204$ million;   3. $25 e^{(-0.15*10)} = 5.578$ million;

5. $-1/2(\ln(1/2)) = 1.386$;   7. $1/2 \ln 4 = 2.7726$;   9. $\dfrac{5600\ln(1/5)}{\ln 2} = 13{,}002.797$;

11. $\dfrac{5600\ln(R/r)}{\ln 2}$;   13. $\dfrac{\ln 2}{0.04} = 17.329$;   15. $(1/r)(\ln(A/P)$

Chapter 4 Review:
1. $\{\{(-2,1),(1,4),(4,7,(7,10)\}$;   2. $x = -3y+4$;   3. $x = 2y^2+3y+1$;   4. yes;

5. no;   6. no;   7. $f^{-1}(x) = \dfrac{4-x}{3}$;   8. $f^{-1}(x) = x^3+2$;   9. $f^{-1}(x) = \ln x$;

10. $f^{-1}(x) = 10^x$;   11. c;   12. d;   13. e;   14. b;   15. a;   16. 2;   17. 3;
18. 2;   19. 3;   20. $x = 3^2$;   21. $b^N = M$;   22. $\log_5(1/25) = -2$;   23. $\ln 40 = x$;

24. $\dfrac{\log 10}{\log 4} = \dfrac{1}{\log 4}$;   25. $2\log x + 4\log y - 5\log z$;   26. 81;   27. -2;   28. 2;

29. 8;   30. 1.

Exercises 5.1
1.

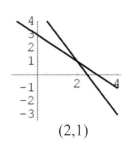

(2,1)

3.

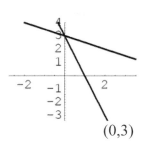

(0,3)

5.

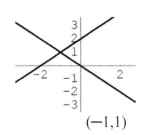

(−1,1)

7. (3, 2);   9. (2, 2);   11. (2, 2);   13. (2, 1);   15. (2, 0);   17. No solution;
19. (2, 0);   20. 10,000, 25,000;   21. 6,000, 9,000;   22. 5, 20;   23. 12.5;
24. 15,000, 5,000.

Exercises 5.2
1. (1, 3, 2);   3. (−1, 2,−3);   5. (−2, −1, 5);   7. (3, 0, − 2);   9. $(1/2, −1/2, 1)$;
11. (2, 3, − 1);   13. (−3, 2, − 1);   15. \$32,000; \$16,000, \$2,000.

Exercises 5.3
1. the shaded area should be above the line, and the line should be dotted;
3. the shaded area should be above the line, and the line should be dotted;
5. the shaded area should be on the right of the line, and the line should be dotted;
7. the shaded area should be above the line, and the line should be dotted;
9. the shaded area should be below the line, and the line should be solid;
11. the shaded area should be on the left of the line, and the line should be solid;
13. the shaded area should be below the line, and the line should be solid;

Exercises 5.4

1. $\begin{bmatrix} 2 & -1 & | & 4 \\ 1 & 3 & | & 4 \end{bmatrix}$;   3. $\begin{bmatrix} 1 & 4 & -2 & | & 5 \\ 1 & 0 & 3 & | & 7 \\ 0 & 2 & 1 & | & 4 \end{bmatrix}$;   5. (2, 1);   7. (0, 1);   9. (3, 1);

11. (1, 1, 1);   13. (−1, 2, −1);   15. (2, 3, 1);   17. (3, 2, −3)

Exercises 5.5

1. $\begin{bmatrix} 0 & 1/2 \\ -1 & 1/2 \end{bmatrix}$;   3. $\begin{bmatrix} 2 & 1 \\ 5 & 3 \end{bmatrix}$;   5. $\begin{bmatrix} -2 & 1 \\ 3/2 & -1/2 \end{bmatrix}$;   7. Inverse does not exist;

9. $\begin{bmatrix} 1/2 & 1/2 & -1/2 \\ -1 & 0 & 1 \\ -1/2 & -1/2 & 3/2 \end{bmatrix}$;   11. $\begin{bmatrix} -15/2 & 4 & 5 \\ 6 & -3 & -4 \\ 2 & -1 & -1 \end{bmatrix}$;   13. $\begin{bmatrix} -1 & 1 & -2 \\ 2 & 0 & 4 \\ 3 & 1 & 5 \end{bmatrix}$;

15. does not exist;   17. (3, −1).

Exercises 5.6:
1. 0;   3. $x^4 − 3x$;   5. 42;   7. $−2s^2 + 5s + 1$;   9. 4, −8, −2;   11. 4, 8, −2;
13. 11;   15. (−24/29, 45/29);   17. (6/41, 16/41);   19. (−7/3, 22/3, 7);
20. (31/5, 19/10, −29/10).

Index